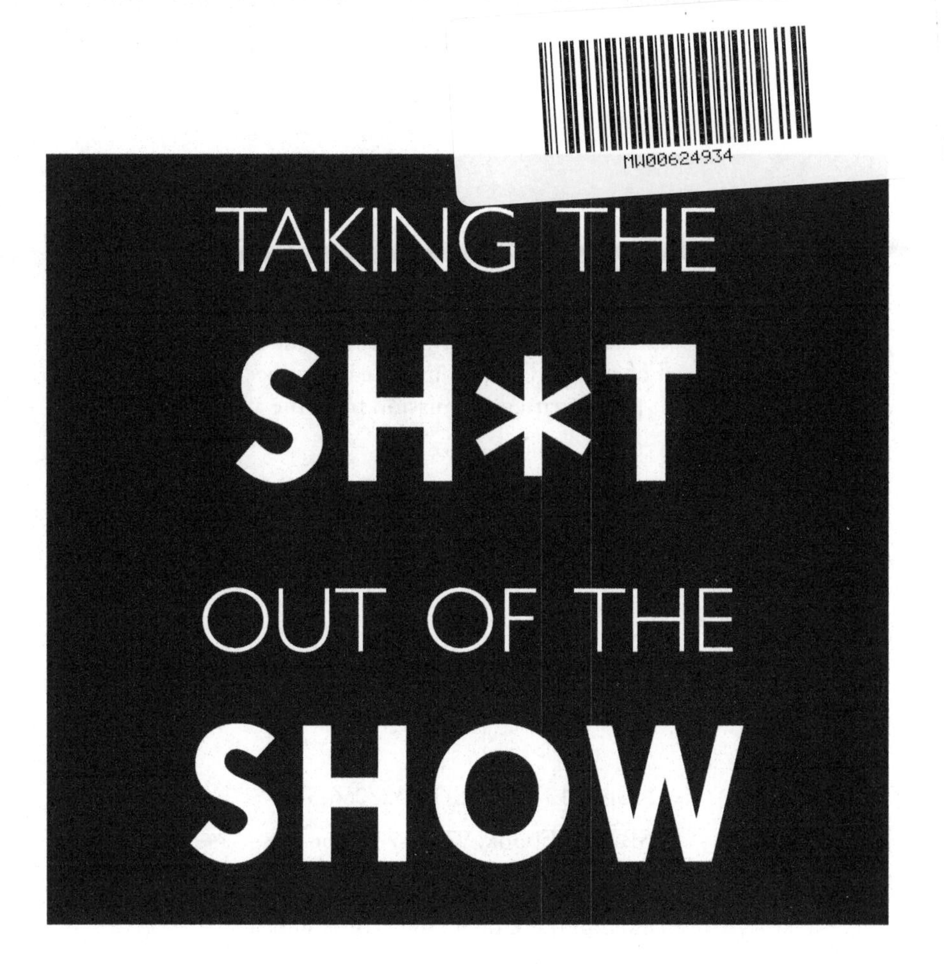

7 Short Stories of How to Navigate Life's Challenges

Danny Bader

*Taking the Sh*t Out of the Show*

Published by Desert Soul Publishing.
www.dannybader.com

Edited by Sue Reynard, www.suereynard.com
Book cover design by Christy Collins, Constellation Book Services.

ISBN 13 TP: 978-1-7327066-5-1
ISBN 13 Ebook: 978-1-7327066-6-8

Printed in the United States of America.

Kara & Priscilla—
Here's to a wonderful year ahead...
and always taking the sh*t out
of the show when needed.
Luv ya.
"Proph"
Nashville
2/22

DEDICATION

To Trish and Bobby

Thank you for the insight, support and LOVE you've provided in helping me—and countless others—take the shit out of our shows and move through the challenges of life.

You are two amazing people—know you are loved tremendously.

– D.

Contents

shitshow

something (such as an event or a situation) that is chaotic, contentious, or unpleasant to an excessive or absurd degree

transition

a change or shift from one state, subject, place, etc. to another

tran-shit-ion

the combination of the two above . . .

I'M SAMMY, YOUR GUIDE . . .

"Only a life lived in the service to others is worth living." – Albert Einstein

I was at a small coffee shop, sipping a cappuccino, reflecting on how I got to where I am.

I'm Samantha Jane Windermere. To an outsider, my life has looked easy. I had parents engaged in my life, went to great schools, got strong grades, and excelled at sports. Did well with my first career.

The only thing was, I'm an only child and my dad really wanted a son. It's partly why everyone calls me Sammy. I remember the first time I became aware of this; I was about six or seven and playing in our living room when I heard my mom and dad talking, well, it was more of an argument. I peered around the corner; my mom was leaning against the kitchen counter, my dad sitting at the table. She spoke clearly, slowly, her voice firm.

"I don't understand you. I know you had your heart set on Sammy being the son you always wanted, and you know what, that's not the case. She's a girl, a beautiful little girl. The fact is you have a wonderful little girl who loves her daddy a ton, and just wants to make you happy. So why do you have to constantly reject her when she asks to spend time with you?"

Dad took a deep breath but didn't answer.

"And you know what," Mom continued, staring at him intensely as she began to leave the room, "you will regret it if you never accept this, and be the type of father she deserves."

My Dad was a prominent businessman where I grew up, and I thought he'd love me more if I tried to follow his path. Hence the Ivy League scholarship, the time on Wall Street and the gobs of money I made, the impressive apartment with a stunning view of Manhattan. None of it made a difference. He still always introduced me, forcing a smile, as the "son he never had."

After my time on Wall Street, I had a bit of what one might call an epiphany or awakening. I realized that I was living in a shitshow, at least part of which was of my own making. So, I moved to Moab, Utah and bought a small restaurant bar from an older couple. It was there that I healed. I healed the hurt little girl still striving for her daddy's love. I did the work I needed to do, with the help of my friend, Brendan, to get to know who "Sammy" really was. It was hard, and fun, and sad, and emotional, and worth it, it was really freakin' worth it.

It was through this work that I realized it is very possible in life to take the proverbial shit out of our show. The wisdom we seek is buried in the struggle. I've looked back at my own struggles and talked with others as they think about their own "how did I get here?" moment of crisis. In that rearview mirror reflection, we beat ourselves up in the quest for "what could I have done differently?" Sometimes, we just did what we thought was right. Other times, we made a choice strongly influenced by something else. Maybe another person, money, alcohol, or drugs. Maybe the aching to simply be accepted, feel a little more worthy, more loved, or just to feel a little better about ourselves.

* * *

And that's the space where I work now: supporting people to move through the shitshows in their lives. I think that word describes it perfectly. I've never heard anyone ask, "What's that?" when I used the word shitshow.

"Shitshow." I said the word softly out loud, smiling and shaking my head at how one simple word can actually give people a very clear picture of what's happening. A guy wearing skinny jeans and flip flops walked by and smiled at me, seemingly amused at the one-word conversation I had with myself. I just smiled back, chuckling.

I'm certainly not laughing at, minimizing, or dismissing what my clients are going through; shitshow describes it well, and they are often brutal struggles for people to get the faith, resilience, trust, and whatever else they need to move through it and survive.

What I strive to point out to my clients is that shitshows are really just transitions. A person needs to move from one place, not literally, to another. They need to move their life, their current state, to another one, a more desirable, graceful one. The definition of transition is the process or a period of changing from one state or condition to another. Our shitshows are the difficult transitions of our life. Transitions filled with chaos, stress, uncertainty, fear, regret, and a long list of many other negative, potentially defeating forces. The other transitions we call our happy times, and my clients don't need me then.

How do I help people through their shitshows? Well, I simply support them in taking the shit out of their show. The shit is not the pain, confusion, chaos, struggle, despair and so on. No, those things exist, and are simply reality. It's not the horrible nature of the facts, nor the transition itself . . . rather, the shit, as I've come to see it, is the manner in which we engage with all this. The shit is our approach to our struggle. The show is just life, in its good times and bad, and the show must always go on. And it does. The question I work with my clients to get answered is, "Is there another way of seeing this? Of engaging with it?" The shit is always there in the beginning, can fade in the middle, and leave little or no residue as we move through. Or it can linger for a long time. I guess I work to shift their perspective to a more productive one.

Right now, I have seven clients, and I'm good with this number. Any more may be too many. I'd like you to meet them . . . .

—1—
Alexis

"Creating more joy and freedom in your life comes from controlling yourself, not others."

- Sammy

Alexis on a Treadmill

Alexis sure wasn't expecting me when I climbed up on the treadmill next to her at a gym several months ago. She was wearing matching black Nike tights and a top, and she ran like an Olympian coming out of the final turn of a 400-meter final. Even the small earphones stuffed in her ears were black. I did an easy three miles, glancing her way a few times. Every now and then she reached back and tightened up her ponytail, then she'd press a button on the glowing control board in front of her and run even faster.

We finished just about the same time and began wiping down the machine. She glanced over and smiled sadly, light shades of black under her eyes. I nodded and as we began to walk away, said, "Have a good day."

"Thanks," she said, "haven't had one of those in a long time."

"Well then, looks like you just had a great run, so I'd say you're off to a good start."

Alexis stopped, wiped her face, and, slowly letting the towel down, began to cry. I grabbed her arm, gently guiding her toward the wooden boxes in the corner of the gym usually used to jump on. That area was empty and the boxes made a great meeting place. She sat, took a few deep breaths, and wiped her eyes.

Looking up, she said, "I feel like I could just run, and not stop. Just keep running."

I remained silent, letting our stillness nudge her to continue.

"Did you ever feel like that?" she asked.

"Oh yes, many times." I smiled. "Many, many times. You don't think I always had this gray hair and these wrinkles around my eyes." She laughed gently, as I extended my hand. "I'm Sammy."

We shook. "I'm Alexis," she replied, "and thank you. I don't usually start crying in front of people I don't know." She paused, shaking her head. "It's just really freakin' hard to control recently."

And this is how I met Alexis. We talked only a few minutes that morning, before going our separate ways.

That was a few months ago. I kept "accidentally" bumping into Alexis at the gym, and eventually our conversations over coffee after the workouts became a regular thing. I explained to her that I was retired now but enjoyed meeting up with friends, acting as a sounding board, and occasionally offering my own insights and advice. She said that was just what she needed, so now we meet once a week, talking and texting in between. Our last two conversations have been particularly important.

So Angry I Can't Think

Alexis and I were meeting as usual at her favorite restaurant, The Birds Nest. Torn white and pink sugar packets lay on the table between us. She was having a bad day, to put it mildly.

I wanted to give her a big hug and tell her it was all going to be okay. Something inside me said not to. Her face was pale, lacking makeup. The small veins in her misty eyes were a bold red, and the hair under her University of North Dakota baseball hat was a mess.

She took a deep breath, slowly exhaled, and said, "He . . . he did it. He. Did. It. He cheated on me. And not just once. I don't deserve any of this. It's just one big shitshow." She paused, her eyes shifting down, and whispered, "I really don't know how I'm gonna get through this. The kids are upset. I'm so angry I can't think."

Alexis stood abruptly and swallowed hard. "And I don't want to talk about it anymore right now."

I reached across the table, taking her hand as she was scooping up her phone and Ray-Bans. I stood, her one hand in mine. With her free hand, Alexis held a crumpled napkin to her nose. She looked at me with sad, tired eyes, shook her head, and walked quickly to the door, getting a few stares from some of our screen-tapping audience.

I sat still, watching. Her head stayed down as she hurried past the guy holding the door for her. She sat behind the wheel of her mini-van as it rolled by, allowing me to catch a glimpse of the empty car seat in the back, and the oval sticker on the back window with the number 13.1 on it. There was no need for me to have stopped her or walked her out. Right then, she just needed time.

Walking to meet Alexis again a week later, I took a deep breath. The air felt different, sweeter, a sign that the gray East Coast winter was releasing its grip. The trees were teasing us with their small green buds, the blue sky looked closer, an occasional flower caught my eye, and two kids on skateboards glided by in shorts and t-shirts. It reminded me of the many springs I'd welcomed during my time working on Wall Street and living in the city. I smiled and exchanged "good mornings" with an older couple walking by as the yellow awnings of the café came into view. I caught sight of Alexis' mini-van parked at the curb, glistening as if it just rolled off the assembly line. *Hmmm*, I thought, *this is weird, she's rarely on time.*

Approaching the café, I saw Alexis sitting at a table near the front window. She looked much better than the week before. She smiled and winked at me as I passed on my way to the front door. As I neared the table, she stood, greeting me with a big hug. Her dark hair was pulled back, a black ribbon holding her ponytail. She wore black slacks; a cream-colored blouse, and subtle make-up colors that enhanced her natural beauty. A silver cross I'd noticed in our last few meetings hung around her neck. Her dark eyes sparkled as she said, "Good morning Sammy, thanks for making the time to meet."

"Yes, absolutely." I replied, "Just explain to me one thing." I paused briefly as Alexis began to sit, her lips together, and head turned. "Where's Alexis, and why do you look like you're on your way to get photographed for the cover of Vogue?"

She rolled her eyes. "Oh, okay, funny, very funny. You had me nervous for a minute."

"Well, you look great."

"Thanks. I had a meeting with my lawyer this morning and have another with the real estate agent after this. Good meeting with my lawyer—she agrees with me that we should really make David pay and do our best to destroy and crush his reputation." She took a deep breath, straightening up in the chair. "So, I just felt like getting dressed up. I guess my yoga pants can stay in the drawer once in a while."

A young male waiter came to our table, took our orders, smiling often at Alexis.

So, I inquired, "How are you?"

She looked around briefly, then back to me as she slid her spoon back and forth on the white tablecloth. "Overall, I'm feeling a little better. After I left you last week, when I was so fixated on saying that he did it, David did it, I realized I was telling everyone else I talked with the same thing. Even as I was folding some laundry, for some reason the phrase *he did it* just kept playing over and over in my mind like a bad recording stuck in a loop. I felt like I'd never be able to move on.

"Why does it take so long?" she continued. "I mean I got suspicious almost a year ago when I caught him lying about a business trip." She took a deep breath, scanning the café. "I was excited to see him after he'd been gone a week, not knowing at the time what his 'meeting' really entailed."

She shook her head, letting out a defeated breath. "I cannot believe I made him his favorite dinner when he came back from that trip because he said it had been such a rough trip, with all the meetings and negotiations. The next day, I happened to call his office and his assistant told me those negotiations had been finalized a month earlier. But I let it slide . . . ."

She closed her eyes, and I could see the tears starting to slide down her cheek. "But a few months ago," she said, "I saw David texting a lot after he'd returned from another business trip." She went on to explain that for some reason—she called it her "women's intuition"—she looked at his phone while he was in the bathroom. The text string was from a younger woman he worked with, and for the most part were about business, until the last one, it said: *I had a nice time.* David's text back was, *Looking forward to our next trip!*

Alexis said there was "just a feeling" that came over her. She began to stalk the woman's social media page, and a few days later saw pictures of her and some others on that "business trip" in Denver. David was in a few, and one showed her and David sitting on a snowmobile, surrounded by a few others. Alexis said the non-verbals in the pictures made her queasy.

I asked her what she did. She said, "I did what any other loving, caring, trusting wife would have done. I hired a private detective." She smiled like a general after winning the battle. "Had him go to Miami, Phoenix, and Denver to follow David—and you know what, the son of a bitch was 3 for 3. Can you imagine? Who does that?"

She said David cried and pleaded with her when she confronted him with one of the pictures, claiming it was only a one-night fling. Alexis had then dropped more pictures on the table in front of him showing him and the woman in different outfits, and said, "It's interesting that you both had wardrobe changes for a one-night fling. Get the hell out of this house. My lawyer will be in contact."

David left that day, though he hadn't moved out of the house yet.

Fighting Through the Storm

"That confrontation must have been tough. Is there any chance you can leave them in the past?" I said. "You reliving those moments is not getting you anything you need to keep going through this, right?"

"I don't know. I wish I could agree, I get it. It's just very hard. But shit, how could I have not known? Meetings and negotiations." She sipped from her mug, then staring into it as she placed it down, fiddling with the silver cross hanging from her neck "I guess I got an F in the awareness test since I found out about the second one a few months after the first. I just should have known."

Alexis' shoulders slumped, her brow tightened, and she went down her road of self-judgement. I reached over, my index and middle finger pulling up her chin. "Hey. Look at me. You were right the other day, and you've been right all along. He did do it. Not you. David is the one that chose to have an affair."

"Affairs." She corrected me with misty eyes.

"Yes, you're right, affairs."

"So, where do I go from here? I actually felt a little better this morning. I was focused on my meetings, and not what happened. Now, here with you, I begin telling myself all the things he did, how I could not have known, and keep trying to figure out why."

"What happens when you do this?"

She wiped her eyes, looking at the black smears on the napkin. "Oh, great, now I'm sure I look wonderful."

Alexis got out a mirror and cleaned the smudges from her face before continuing.

"What happens when my mind starts racing with the thoughts of what I could've done differently, maybe been a better wife? When I can't get rid of the thoughts of him sleeping with someone else? I don't know, all I know is when I get like this there's a sharp pain in my stomach, and I feel like I could vomit."

Our meals came and I began to eat. Alexis seemed to have lost her appetite. After a few moments, she spoke again. "Lucy and Thomas know something is wrong, and I can tell it's affecting them. This is the last thing I ever wanted, I want my kids to grow up normal, and be happy. Lucy asked the other day why Daddy was sleeping in Pop-Pop's room. That's what she calls the guest room because my dad stays there when he comes to visit."

"What did you tell her?"

"I told her it's because Daddy's sick." She took a small bite of her omelet. "I guess it's not a total lie, he's so selfish, and he is one sick son-of-a . . . " Alexis stopped talking and began to cry. I let her go, as I knew I had to. Quite often I've seen people say things like, "It's okay, stop crying honey," or something like that, and while they mean well, it's not okay. It has the potential to all be okay, just not now. One cannot shorten the path needed for us to move through our shitshows.

We finished our meals, although Alexis seemed to have lost her appetite as the movie of David's infidelity played in her mind, and she moved more of the food around on her plate than she actually ate.

"Do you have a few more minutes?" I asked as I saw the waiter coming to bring our check. "There's one thing I want to show you before we leave."

"Sure, Nina said she can watch the kids 'til about two and then she has to leave for class. That girl sure is a huge help for me now."

"Great." I replied as the waiter cleared our plates. We ordered a fresh cup of coffee, and I slid my chair around the table to be next to

Alexis. I pulled the notepad from my bag, the one with my initials in navy across the top. I like dark blue and white, just so classic to me.

Noticing them, she asked, "What's your middle name?"

"Jane."

"OK, that's cool. Samantha Jane Windermere. I like it. A strong name."

I smiled, "Yep, when I was older my mom would always joke, 'Well, at least he agreed to a girl's name in the middle.'"

Our coffee was poured, steam rising from the mug, and I turned the small pad sideways for more room and began to write. I wrote the word transition, leaving a blank between the letters "s" and "i." I asked, "What do you see?"

Alexis held her mug closely to her lips, wrapped in both hands, and staring at my notepad replied. "Hmmmm, I feel like there may be a trick here."

I smiled, "No trick, perhaps just a simple lesson."

"Hmmm, I see the word transition." Then after a sip she finished her observation. "And I feel like you're Vanna White, and I'm playing Wheel of Fortune or something. There's a space in there after the 's.'" I nodded. "Why?"

"Well, let's see. Before we do I want you to close your eyes." She did, smiling slightly, and I wrote a letter in the blank. "OK, you can open."

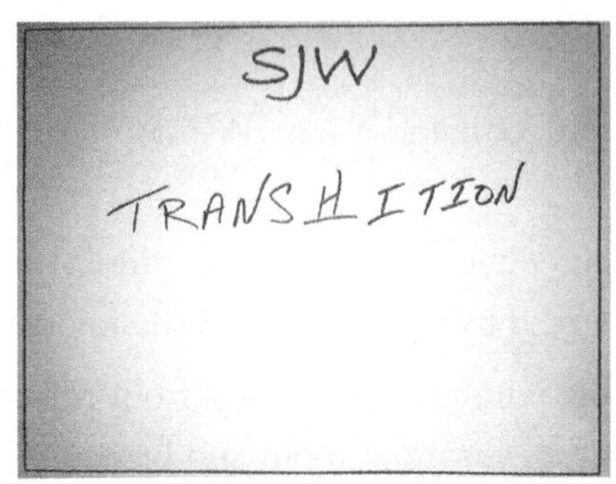

Alexis looked at the word for a few seconds, and then asked, laughing, "Why did you put the shit in transition?" I laughed along with her as a few café patrons looked our way. "When you added the 'h' that word within the word just jumps out at me."

"Right, let's talk about that." I smiled. "What I've come to realize is our lives, your life, is always just a series of transitions, our having to, or wanting to move from one state, one situation in life to another."

"Makes sense." Alexis murmured, again wrapping both hands around her mug, and taking a sip. "If you look at it that way, I guess you could say that every day when we wake up is a transition. Right?"

"I think so."

"OK, but why put the shit—so to speak—in it?"

"Ah." I smiled, "this seems to be the main question that I deal with in my work of supporting you and others. I don't put that in. You see, the 'shit', for me is not the often-brutal facts of the situation the person is facing. It's not the pain and struggle and uncertainty of the transition, it's simply how one chooses to be when they deal with it, how they think about it and what they do."

Alexis' mouth twitched. She bit her bottom lip and squinted her eyes. She looked away, then back to me, her gaze urging me to continue. "You see, Alexis, the shit is almost always in the transition the person is dealing with, it seems we're wired as people to focus a bit more on the negative nature of it, and it's captured perfectly in the word you're fond of using: *shitshow.*"

She smiled like a young student that finally gets the equation the teacher has written on the board. "I got it . . . I think. You're saying that the actual thing—like my pending divorce—the transition that someone is dealing with, the thing they're in, is always gonna have struggle, regret, and pain and confusion, and so on," she said. "Those things will remain. The power in this, the growth available to us comes from how we view them."

Alexis, took a deep breath, shaking her head, "It sure does make sense, and a pretty simple a way to get the point across. But the reality of being in the middle of this shitshow is just so hard; for me right now it feels impossible to be rational about this."

She paused, then finished with a grin, "I guess the key is taking the shit out of the show. . . . And taking the 'h' out of that word."

We both laughed, "Yes, that would be the key," I said. "The show, that is the struggle and challenge that you or anyone else is in must go on, it has too. It's just life, right?" She nodded. "Your divorce is an outcome that will happen along that path, and I know you do not want it, not many really want their shitshows. I suggest you consider looking at your transition . . . "

"You mean transhi . . . transit . . . tran-*shit*-shun. Wow that's tough to say." She interrupted.

"Yes, it is, right? And tough to deal with. Yours is not so much the divorce itself, it's all you must do to grow and persevere through and past it. Make sense?"

Alexis nodded.

"OK, I know you have to run and get home for the kids. But I have a task for you that I think will help if you're up for it."

"Sure."

"Good. Here it is: You have to make a list of all the negative things about the way you're dealing with your divorce, your unfaithful husband, the kids, your self-image, your worrying about what other people think, everything going on for you right now. Don't describe each of these aspects of your situation. Rather, think about how you're dealing with them. There are no right or wrong answers here. Just reflect on your thinking, and the little voice you told me about that runs non-stop in your head."

Alexis smiled. "What if there are *voices*?" she said, emphasizing the plurality of the word. "I have a few of them up there."

I chuckled and nodded. "Yes, get them all. Listen to them all. Write down what they're telling you, what they say. Write down what you do, the actions you take throughout your day, and with the kids. Write down some of the things you say to your friends, and others supporting you, and write down what they say to you. Pay attention to when you have good energy, and when you don't. Got it?"

"I think so. Maybe you can help me get started right now before we leave. Can I make the list on my phone?"

"Sure."

Alexis grabbed her phone, holding it in front of her, thumbs ready like an eager student who decades ago would have held a #2 pencil.

"Think about our time together just now, over the past hour," I said. "What do you think had a negative nature to it in the way you're moving through this challenge in your life, what David did, and the impact it's having on your life?"

She took a deep breath through her nose, letting it out through her mouth, then looking to me. "I don't know, this is hard. I feel like I was okay today."

"Good, let's think about this. You're okay today. Does that imply that some days you're not okay?"

"Absolutely."

"Right, and let me remind you of something else you said earlier. Remember you said you probably got an "F" in awareness because you didn't know about David's affairs?" Alexis nodded; her gaze intently focused on me. "What word describes what you're doing when you do this?"

Alexis sat for a moment, shook her head, "I'm not sure."

I smiled. "That's OK. How about the word judgment?"

"Yes, yes, that is a good one. I mean, not a good one, it's a negative word . . . shit, you know what I mean. I'm putting that on the list."

"Great, you got it. You see how you're judging yourself? Doing that does not put you in a good place for resilience and perseverance, which is what you need to move through this rough time—especially when you give yourself a failing grade."

"But the things I'm judging did happen. David did cheat and I ignored all the warning signs. That's all true."

"Yes," I replied. "But instead of thinking about yourself as a failure, how about you just think about that past event as just history.

It happened the way it did. You can't change that. But you *can* look for ways to grow stronger and improve, just not beat yourself up in the process."

She nodded, her eyes tearing, "And I know I'm in judgment of him and what he did. What he did to me, and our family, and the kids. It was wrong, and right now, Sammy, I gotta tell you I'm still going to judge the bastard. Some things are just plain wrong."

We stood, and I gave her a hug, then pulled back, holding her arms. "Just do the homework, at your own pace, become more aware of what you're thinking and doing and saying and just get it on the list." I smiled, adding, "And without judgment, right?"

Alexis wiped an eye, looking at me sadly, "I guess I'll try, not sure I can do it."

You Don't Own Other People's Actions

About a week later, as the sun was sneaking up, I was talking with my boss. I guess you can call her my boss; she's the one I update about my friends/clients and what's happening in their lives. We were interrupted when my phone buzzed. I saw a text from Alexis.

> Alexis: Can you talk. That son-of-a-bitch wants custody.

I told my boss I'd get back to her then fiddled with my phone, finally touching Alexis' name to initiate a call. She answered right away and was crying. "Sammy. Can you believe his lawyer has filed for custody? I mean, come on, how do they think they can get this? He's the one that was unfaithful. I didn't do anything. Shit, what judge would ever give him the kids? I'm telling you, if this happens, I'm gonna lose it."

Crying and sniffing was all I heard for a minute. "Where are you?" I asked.

"I'm at home. The kids are with my friend for a while."

"Okay, sit tight. Give me your address and I'll be there as fast as I can. We'll figure this out."

When I arrived, Alexis was standing in the front doorway, wearing black tights and a baggy sweatshirt, another crumpled tissue in hand. She lunged at me and hugged me tight, sobbing, "I can't deal with this. I cannot let him get the kids."

As we let go, I pulled a tissue from my jacket pocket and wiped her eyes, handing it off to her. "Come, let's sit." I led her into the house and onto the couch looking out at the back yard. The swings on the set swayed gently, and a few kickballs dotted the grass.

Alexis was looking straight out the window, then turned, taking a deep breath, "The shit in my show just got even more real. What am I gonna do?" she paused, "What are we going to do?"

"OK, OK. Tell me what happened."

"I don't know, really. I guess his lawyer thinks he can get them. I mean, there's no way, with all the travel he does, that he could be good for them." She stood, pacing the length of the window. I got up this morning and dropped the kids with my friend to play with her kid for a while. I came home and was feeling pretty good. I was working on my homework for you and was really paying attention to my thoughts, how I was seeing my transition, and I felt better, I just felt a little better. And then," she stopped and mumbled under her breath something I could not hear. "And then my lawyer calls and tells me she just got word from David's lawyer that he is filing for custody."

I remained silent.

"I just can't believe it," Alexis continued. "I mean he hurts me so much with the affairs, and now he wants to hurt me even more. Why? Just why? What did I do to deserve this?"

I stood, walking in front of her as she stopped. "Alexis, hear this." I grabbed her forearms firmly, "Really hear me. If there is one I thing I know, it's this. *People are gonna do what they're gonna do, and say what they're gonna say.*" She pulled away, walking to the window.

"Alexis, David is going to do what he is going to do, and say what he is going to say," I said. "Nothing," I took a deep breath and made my tone even firmer, "nothing you did, or will do is going to change that. He had those affairs, not you." She turned to me. "Yes, he had the affairs. And you know what? If he was married to someone else, he likely would have done the same thing."

She stared at me for a few seconds, seemingly processing my last sentence. "But what about the kids?" she almost wailed. "I need them. I'll be crushed without them."

"Yes, I know. Let's put this custody thing aside for just one minute, can we?"

She yelled at me, "No, no Sammy, we can't. This is the shit in the show, to put it in your language, and I gotta take it out." Silence filled the room as she sat back down on the couch. A few minutes passed, as we both stared out the window, some birds darting back and forth from the trees to the swing set, and a white cat scampering across the back corner of the yard under some bushes.

Alexis turned to me. "Sorry. I know you're here to help me."

"No sorry needed, I get it." Placing my hand on her knee, I offered, "Alexis, here's the thing you really want to consider. What he did had nothing to do with you." She breathed deeply, shaking her head. "Trust me, it didn't."

I continued, "You're owning what David did, and you don't need to. He does. You cannot own the actions of another. That's a path to nowhere. You can only own what you control, and you cannot . . . you *did not* control what he did, or what he is doing now."

She sat, her hand on her silver cross.

I nodded to it. "You've been wearing that cross a lot more." I paused, then asked, "Fashion statement?"

"Nope. I figured I need to get some of my faith back, it's been a while."

"Sounds like a great idea to me. I've seen Faith be a great foundation for strength for many people." I smiled with a wink and asked, "Do you have any coffee?"

Once the steaming mugs were sitting on the kitchen table in front of us, Alexis picked up where we had left off. "I guess what you say is right, it's just hard to see it that way."

"What I say is what I say. The rightness or wrongness of it comes from your perspective. And, again, this is judgment. It's just another way of looking at it, which is perspective, right? There have been some people who were cheated on and I've heard others say they deserved it. They say they were not a good husband, or a good wife."

"Do you agree?"

"Not anymore. A long time ago, back in my days on Wall Street, maybe. Now though, I just believe people don't deserve to be hurt. If the relationship is not good, get help . . . or get out. Alexis, you have a choice here. And this is where you can take some of your shit out of your show. How do you want to handle this request for custody, and this whole transition you're in?"

She fiddled with her mug, sliding it in a small circle on the table. "I don't really know. I just want Lucy and Thomas." Her eyes filled with tears. "I'll be lost without them, I mean I feel so lost now, I can't even imagine only seeing them once a week, or whatever."

She went on. "My lawyer said this is so wrong, and we should just crush him. And part of me really wants to do that. He's such a jerk. Do you know we named Lucy after David's great grandmother? Thomas is named after David's father, and then his middle name is David. David calls him TD." Shaking her head, she said, "I may have told you that David went to Stanford and brags about playing football. Well, I found out recently that although he was on the team, he never really got in the games much. But anyway, he wants Thomas to go to Stanford, and play football. He always says, *can't you hear the announcer saying, 'and there's another Cardinal touchdown, I guess we could say it's another TD for TD.'* He thinks that's cool. It's so stupid. And I think, I know, that David would enjoy the TD more than Thomas. I'm not sure Thomas is even gonna like sports."

Alexis apologized for getting sidetracked, then said, "I'm getting lost in the details. What do you think I should do about the custody thing?"

"What do you want?" I asked. "Do you want to crush him? Do you want to pray he has a heart attack?" She smiled devilishly for just a second before I continued, "You know the words we use impact our physiology, and our attitudes."

"Sometimes I want to do bad stuff to him, to hurt him like he hurt me." She stopped, looked up and ran her hand through her hair. "What I really want is for all of this to be over, and I want the kids to be with me."

"Great, I like that. So how about you . . . how about *we* . . . focus on that? You see, I believe we get what we focus on, and when we hold the image of what we want it puts us in a good energy, a good feeling and emotion, and that's the place from which we take action." I let her process that, then offered, "While logic plays a part in some choices, most people tell me that most of the time they're more likely taking action based on how they feel."

"Makes sense. So what should I do?"

"Well, what would someone do who was focused *not* on crushing or hurting anyone—even when that person hurt them—but rather on moving through the hurt and the situation to a better place? And" I added, "having custody of her two kids?"

Alexis smiled for a moment, stood, and said, "She'd get a shower and go meet with her lawyer, and begin to make a very clear, objective case as to why she should have the kids."

"Good. How about you do just that, and call me afterward?"

"You got it," she said, giving me a quick hug on her way to the stairs.

Later that day as I sat in stillness on a brick patio, enjoying the warmth of the Spring sun on my face, my phone buzzed. Opening my eyes, I focused for a moment on the small pink and white flowers dotting a nearby bush. I looked at my phone and read the text from Alexis.

> Alexis: hey Sammy. thanks again for the time today. I told my lawyer I really didn't want to hurt David or crush him. I just wanted to get what I deserve out of the marriage financially and most importantly I need to have Lucy and Thomas with me, and I want to move on and have this be over
>
> Me: This is great. So glad you're working to see this whole thing differently than a few months ago. What are your next steps?
>
> Alexis: We have a meeting with David and his lawyer next week. Can we meet in next few days? I want to go over my homework with you.
>
> Me: Absolutely. I'll be in touch

Ready to Move Forward

It would be nice to say that Alexis' experience was smooth sailing after that. But we all know the real world doesn't work that way. David stalled over moving out of the house, but eventually gave in. There was still a lot of wrangling over custody—and her husband's lawyer threatened to bring up a decades-old DUI driving ticket that Alexis had received. But *her* lawyer shot that down quickly. ("Do you think the judge will be more influenced by Alexis' one-time poor choice, or a married, father of two young children repeated, premeditated pattern of adultery?")

Still, when we met on a summer's morning, Alexis was proud of her progress.

"Can we go over some of that homework you gave me?"

"Sure. What did you come up with?"

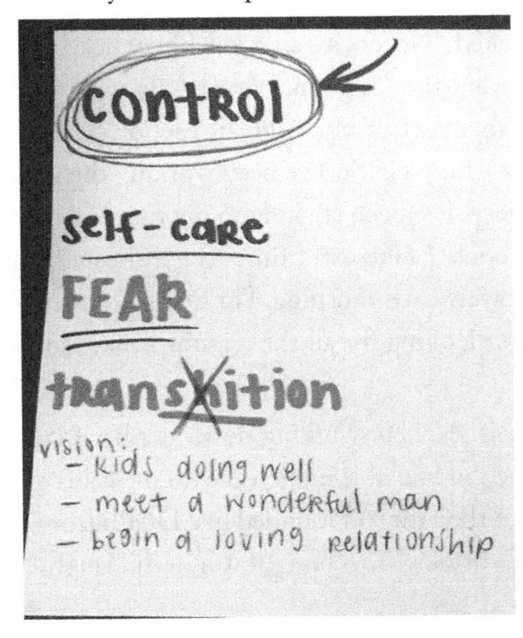

"Well, a lot. This really was a powerful exercise for me, and it is something I need to work on for sure. It was good for me to reflect on all the support you've given me. And the times you challenged me; challenged my thinking and perspective. I feel so much better, and nothing about my situation has really changed. I still have some work to do on becoming more self-aware, and things to take care of, this ain't over yet."

"Great, what are the main things you learned, or were reminded of?"

"The first one is definitely about me not owning what David did. I've really worked to not focus on that as it only freaked me out. Instead," she looked to her paper, and circled the word *control* a few times, that was written in big, bold, black marker. "I now realize the power for me when I just focus on what I can control. I have to—and I'm good with this now—own my situation, just not what he did. I also kept hearing your voice in my head."

Squinting my eyes, I said, "Uh oh."

Alexis winked. "No, no, it's all good. I kept hearing you say, 'People are gonna say what they're gonna say, and do what they're gonna do.' I also realized that part of my original reaction to all this shit was to stop taking care of myself. So I've been working the past few weeks on getting more sleep. I've been sticking to my running routine and eating more healthy foods. I take extra time to get dressed, and I'm back to saying a few prayers each morning. I'm focused on feeling good about myself instead of looking for all the reasons I may have contributed to all of this."

I nodded, as she kept working down her list. "And that time you told me what he did had nothing to do with me is becoming believable for me. At first, I thought you sounded like Dr. Phil, or Oprah, or one of those other TV shrinks." This bought wonderful laughter from us both.

"Oh, and this one was huge, and maybe the hardest. Just as I'm trying hard to not judge my past actions, I'm also trying to not judge David for what *he* did. In my eyes, it was wrong, very wrong, and it still is, and I'll always think this way. It's just that judging him was like me making him know it was wrong too, and I guess I just can't do that anymore. I can't control what he thinks, nor do I want to. I have to accept it as part of my past."

Glancing down I saw the words FEAR and transhition written in red. "How about the fear?"

"Yeah, working on that. It's still here. I get scared of what might happen with those two," she pointed her pen in the direction of the kids. "And what if I never meet anyone? I said I'd rather be alone, but . . . I know now I'm gonna want to meet someone, I need to. And truth be told, these two scare me." She paused, taking a bite of her taco. "Any thoughts?" she asked as she chewed.

"Sure. Fear is going to be around, I get it. A strong strategy to deal with it is to see what you're scared of, in this case, the kids being messed up from all this, or you being alone and not finding someone to love, and love you back. Then take the time to imagine the opposite, just reverse the picture. See the kids doing well, see yourself meeting a wonderful man, and beginning a loving relationship." Alexis was nodding and making some notes, "Then," I paused, waiting for her to look at me. "Then, you have got to take action, you have got to do one thing, just one thing, that will move you toward the good vision you want in your future."

Alexis, walked to the sink, filling her glass with water, and returning to the table. "And this," she pointed the tip of her pen to the big green X that crossed out the 'h' in the word transhition. All of this that I'm talking to you about is helping me take the 'h' out. It helps me take the shit out of the show."

Smiling, I grabbed the paper from her and wrote:

From h_______ to ____________________

Alexis tilted her head slightly, as I moved the page in front of her. "Let's do one final little exercise. What word, beginning with an 'h' represents where you're moving from? Remember, transition is simply the movement, the progression from one place to another. Take a minute or two with this. I'll go check on those guys." I smiled, pointing my finger toward the other room. About 10 minutes later I returned, glancing down to see the page in front of Alexis.

"This was good, almost like one thought that covers everything, and brings it into one simple line. Here, take a look." She turned the page and pushed it toward me.

From hunkered down to let's
gooooooooooooo

control
no judgement!!
self-care
FEAR
From hunkered down to
let's goooooooooooooo
transition
vision:
- kids doing well
- meet a wonderful man
- begin a loving relationship

"So? Do you like it?"

"Absolutely. Tell me about it."

Alexis breathed deeply, stretching her hands over her head, then folding them on the table. "I see it like this, when all this happened, and we first met on the treadmills, I was so lost and angry and confused and guilty and damaged and hopeless and regretful and judging, and all that. There was no way I could move forward. To me, I was hunkered down, I was digging in for a fight. A fight based on all those negative emotions, and that's all I ever thought about." Shaking her head and pointing to the words 'hunkered down' she said, "This was killing me. With your help, and inspiration, I began to let go of some of that, and trust me, Sammy, I still have work to do, and I'm still in a fight, it's just I'm fighting it differently, from a new perspective. I know it doesn't change magically to unicorns and rainbows," she paused, emphasizing her next word slowly, "and, doing the work, as you call it, has given me a way forward, so'" she moved the pen to the right side of her statement, "let's gooooooooooo."

She stood and came to me, her arms outstretched, "Thank you Sammy." We hugged a moment, then she and the kids walked me to my car. Alexis said she'd let me know what she heard about the trial, and everything else, saying we'd meet again then.

We'd exchanged a few texts during the week, then Friday about lunchtime my phone buzzed, showing Alexis' picture. I answered to the sound of her crying happily. "I got them, Sammy, I got them. Lucy and Thomas are staying with me." She continued, telling me that David's attorney said they wanted to settle out of court, and after one final meeting that just happened, all the financial and custody issues were resolved, and her divorce is final. We met the next morning for coffee, both smiling easily as a big part of Alexis' transition was over. Alexis said she was going to be busy for a few weeks, so we agreed to stay in touch with calls and texts, and meet in about a month for dinner to celebrate.

I arrived at the restaurant first, getting a high-top table in the bar area near the front window. I watched Alexis enter and noticed several patrons watch her as well. Her hair fell in soft curls below her shoulders, and she wore white jeans, flip flops, and a navy silk, sleeveless blouse.

We hugged, "You look amazing."

Taking her seat, she winked, "Thank you Sammy, navy and white in your honor."

We ordered a nice Pinot Noir from Oregon, feeling the need for a small celebration. Alexis caught me up on the kids; the new job she would be starting in a week; her transition to being divorced, and the 'homework' she continued to do. She said there were some friends that wanted to set her up on a blind date, she was just going to wait a while for that one. Her final story was vintage Alexis, "I have to tell you something. Something I had to do as my last act of moving out of hunkered down mode."

"Okay." I said, "I can't wait for this, given that mischievous grin glued to your face."

"Ha, ha, really? Me? Mischievous?" She took a sip of wine, then continued, "It was a few weeks ago and David texted me to see if I could get a sitter and I could come down to the hotel where he was staying just to talk for few minutes. He bought a condo not far away, and is having it renovated, you know him."

I said nothing, swirling my wine, and nodding. "And?"

"And I went." He was having a drink in the bar—probably not his first. He went on to tell me how much he'd been thinking, and how he wished he could go back and change things, and blah, blah, blah. I began to say some things I really wanted to say. You know, about how much he hurt me, and I was going to tell him about my homework."

She shook her head, "He wasn't paying any attention and kept interrupting me." Alexis took a sip, peering over the rim of her wineglass, "So I got an idea."

"An idea?" I asked nervously.

"Yes, an idea. I said we should go to his room and just talk, alone."

"Oh no, you didn't?"

"Well, sort of. On our walk to the elevator, he smiled and placed his arm around my shoulder."

"Oh no."

Alexis was smiling, her expression one I could not read.

"Sammy, your eyes just got the size of apples. Calm down, it's okay, let me finish, let me finish."

"Do I have a choice?"

"No.

An enormous smile covered her face. "At the elevator I stop. I know what he's thinking, so I lean in like I'm going to kiss him and stop short of his lips, and say, 'David, you know what?' and he whispers, 'What?' Then I said, 'This is not gonna happen, not tonight, not ever again. I just needed to get your attention, and now that I have it. You did hurt me, you hurt me real bad. 'And you know what else?' I continued, not giving him a second to respond. 'You cannot hurt me anymore. I can control that for sure. And you know another what?' I said, as I moved a little closer like a boxer looking for the knockout. David just stood there, wearing a sad, dumb look on his face. Then I said, 'I bet—big time—that you're going to come to realize all of your running around, all of the women, and the other stuff you did to get you something you believed I could not give you . . . you will come to believe that ultimately'—and I shook my head when I said this—'all you did was hurt yourself.' I took a deep breath and delivered a line I'd rehearsed about 30 times. 'You were not a good man, not a good father, not a good husband. How about now, now you work your ass off to be a great ex-husband, and a great father?' I reached past him, pushing the elevator button, and finished with just two words. Your choice. Then I turned and walked out."

I sat there, my mouth open, just shaking my head and raising my wine glass to toast her. We clinked glasses, took a sip, and Alexis continued.

"You know what happened then?"

I shook my head, wine glass still in my hand.

"That little voice in my head you talk about?" She paused, grinning as I nodded. "Well, turns out it wasn't so little. It actually sounded like an excited announcer at a World Cup Soccer match. It screamed "Ladies and gentlemen, Alexis is back!"

—2—

Nigel

"Keep going, because you didn't come this far to only come this far."

- Unknown

Nigel Is Broken

I finally passed through the customs gate at Toronto's Pearson airport, breathing a sigh of relief. For some reason, I always get nervous about my passport. You know, like it's not going to pass muster. Thankful I hadn't checked any luggage; I texted my friend Eva who had said she'd send a car for me. Her reply told me to walk out past the taxi stands and look for a black Range Rover. I was squinting in the late afternoon sun as I exited the terminal door, then pulled up quickly as a large black SUV screeched to a halt in front of me, the tinted windows concealing the driver. The door opened slowly and out stepped Eva.

"Hello, Sammy! Wonderful to see you again." I shook my head as she moved in for a hug. "Well, who were you expecting? I was not going to send my driver for you. I moved a few meetings around, and here I am." She held out her hands and did a twirl.

Eva's short brown hair had wisps of blond. Large black sunglasses sat above her infectious smile, and her pantsuit was a deep purple, the color of eggplant. She lifted her pant leg to show me her leopard print high heels. "And how about these babies? Just picked them up the other day. We'll have to get you a pair."

"They're so you. I love them. You look great, as always," I said as I climbed into the passenger seat. Eva and I had met in another lifetime many years ago at the Tuscany Wellness Center for Children in Moab, Utah. She's the CEO of a large children's hospital in Toronto and, in fact, was taking me there to see a young patient named Chloe (though it was really her father, Nigel, who needed some help).

"You look wonderful, too, Sammy." She winked. "As you always do. You'll have to let me in more on your secret when you can." I took a deep breath as the Range Rover danced between vehicles. "It sure seems a coincidence that your Chloe is being treated at our hospital. I was happy when you emailed me and told me someone had told you about her and her father. You'll love her. She's a wonderful young lady, and a bit full of piss and vinegar."

"So I've heard. And remember my dear, coincidence, according to Einstein, is God's way of staying anonymous."

Eva glanced to me, then her tone grew more somber as she looked at the road. "Well, our Chloe sure could use a little help from God right now. And Nigel is taking everything badly, which I guess is understandable since he got Chloe's diagnosis so soon after losing his wife—" She pursed her lips, then changed subjects. "So, tell me how everything is going with you."

We filled the rest of ride with chitchat. I watched the buildings roll by as we made our way through the city. When we got to the hospital, Eva immediately escorted me to Chloe's room. The young girl leapt from the chair in the corner, hurrying to Eva for a hug.

"Well, hello, Princess, how are you today?" asked Eva.

"I'm okay. Just wish they would let me have more iced coffee; the nurse said the doctors said no."

"Well, we have to listen to the nurses," said Eva. "They're the ones in charge around here, you know." Chloe pulled away, frowning at Eva, who reluctantly gave in. "OK, I'll see what I can do. But now, let me introduce you to my friend Samantha. Everybody calls her Sammy."

"Hello, Sammy," Chloe said as she held out her hand. "I'm Chloe."

I smiled at the formality, something I've seen a lot with children who spend a lot of time around adults. We shook hands. "Hello Chloe. I'm happy to meet you. Eva has told me a lot about you."

"Don't believe any of it. Miss Eva makes a lot of stuff up about me," she said, pointing her finger playfully at Eva, who gave her a kiss on the head then turned to leave. "I have to run. I'll leave you two to talk for a while. Sammy, I'll be back in a half-hour to pick you up so we can go meet Nigel." She left the room, but popped her head back in after a few seconds. "Be sure to ask Chloe about Seamus. They're getting married." She stuck her tongue out at Chloe and disappeared.

Chloe jumped up on the bed in her sweatpants and red and black hoodie bearing the Toronto FC logo. Someone in the family was obviously a soccer fan. "You can sit in the chair if you'd like."

I settled in, smiling. "So, Seamus is the lucky man."

She grinned. "Remember what I said. Miss Eva makes a lot of stuff up."

"Tell me about Seamus."

"Oh, we're just friends," she replied as her gaze wandered around the room. "He lives in Montreal. We met because our doctors know one another and we're both kind of sick with the same thing. Eva just teases me about . . ." She stopped suddenly as her gaze returned to me. "Why are you glowing? It's weird."

Her comment caught me off guard, and I stammered, "Gl . . . Glowing? Oh, I guess . . . I guess it's these fancy hospital lights bouncing off my old gray hair."

"You don't look too old."

I chuckled. "Oh, thanks Chloe. Trust me, I'm a lot older than I look." I rummaged in my purse and pulled out a bag of candy bars, handing it to Chloe. "I'm told you're a fan of Snickers."

"For sure!" She took the bag. "Thank you, Sammy, these are my favorite. Would you like one?"

I nodded and she reached into the bag and handed one to me then grabbed another for herself.

"My mom and me used to eat these all the time. She liked them when we would freeze them first." She opened the wrapper quickly, but paused before putting the candy bar into her mouth.

I opened my own candy bar and after chewing a few bites said, "Miss Eva told me about your mother. I am really sad for you, Chloe. And I promise I'm going to do all I can to help Miss Eva, and everyone help you get you better."

She stopped mid-bite and looked deep into my eyes with the gaze of someone who is much older than her years. "That would be really good for my dad."

"I'm sure it would be. Tell me, how is your dad? I'm about to go meet him."

"He's not so good a lot of times," said Chloe. "He's sad. He's been sad since my mom died three years ago in that accident. And now I'm here. He always says, 'What have I done to deserve this?'" She began fiddling with the bag of candy. "I do my best to use happy words when I talk to him. It makes me feel better, and I want him to be happier too. Does that sound weird? My dad's been mad ever since my mom . . . um, left us. He tries to spend a lot of time with me, but he usually just stares into space and doesn't respond when I ask him questions. Like he isn't really there, if you know what I mean." I nodded.

Chloe settled back on her bed. "He works a lot at a pub. A lot. He says he needs to work long hours to make money for my treatment." She looked out the door into the empty hallway. "But I think it's also so he doesn't have to come here. It makes him sadder."

Eva appeared at the door. "Something's come up and I can't go with you to meet Nigel, but my driver, Peter, will take you. Are you two finished here or should I tell Peter to wait?"

"I certainly want to talk to Chloe more, but I'd also like to meet her father. Chloe, would it be OK if I came back soon to visit you again?" She nodded. I stood and smiled at Chloe. "Can I get a hug?" She happily complied.

I was settled in the rear seat of Eva's car and raised my voice so the young man in the driver's seat could hear me. "Do you know the pub we're going to, Peter?"

He looked at me in the rearview mirror. "Sure, been there a few times," he said with a wink. "Great pub. Feels just like you've been transported to Britain. Everybody drinks pints and watches soccer—or football as they call it there. Toronto FC all the way!"

I laughed. "Sounds like fun."

We chatted until Peter pulled the car in front of the pub and got out to open the door for me. I climbed out and we entered the pub. We stood inside the door, scanning the tables and booths on the left, and the long, full bar on the right. The walls and ceiling were a dark wood, and soccer games played on every TV, and colorful jerseys hung from the ceiling.

I jumped when a man grabbed Peter from behind. Two men sitting at the bar turned to watch as Peter wiggled to break free before the man let go and the struggle turned into a hug. "Hey there, Pete. It's about time you came back for a visit."

"Hi, Sebastian. Good to see you." Turning to me he said, "This is Eva's friend, Miss Sammy. She's here to meet Nigel."

He took my hand in a firm shake. "Hello Sammy. Eva told me about you. It's nice to meet you and welcome to my pub. I don't have to put the 'miss' in front of your name like Pete here, eh? I believe he does because of that suit he wears and the fancy car he drives." He punched Peter's shoulder.

"Sammy is just fine, Sebastian," I said.

"Let me get you seated then I'll introduce you to Nigel. Pete, are you staying, too?"

"Nope, I have a few more errands to run for Eva. She just texted and said her meeting ended early so she grabbed an Uber and will be here soon. Bye, Sammy. I'll be back to pick up you and Eva in a little bit. See you later, Sebastian."

As I followed Sebastian towards an empty stool near the end of the bar, I noticed one bartender moving quickly, pulling on the taps and placing full pints of beer in front of patrons lined up at the bar. He was lean, gliding around as if doing a dance he'd rehearsed a thousand times. His brown hair hung below his collar; he didn't smile. His sad eyes glanced at me for a split second as I slid onto the stool at the end of the bar. Sebastian raised his arm and the bartender appeared. "Nigel, take care of my friend, Sammy, here."

"Hello Ma'am," Nigel said, his face stoic and tan. "What will you have?"

"Hi Nigel, I'm Sammy." I held out my hand, taking his and feeling the years of labor in the roughness. "Just a pint will be okay. Whatever you're pouring." He nodded, reached for a glass without looking, and took two more orders from patrons as he filled my glass. The pint appeared in front of me, without a word or look from Nigel. For a few minutes I watched him move in silence behind the bar, a seemingly perpetual scowl on his face. A few minutes later, I caught sight of Eva at the door. She made her way to me, stopping to hug a few people in her path.

"Sammy, my dear, sorry I got delayed. You're okay though?" she said smiling, "Not the first time you had to pass some time in a pub."

Nigel stopped in front of us. "Hey Eva. Glass of wine?"

"Hello, Nigel, good to see you." She nodded and he placed a glass of red wine on a napkin in front of Eva.

"Anything else you need?" he asked. "Sebastian said you might get a bite to eat."

"Yes, yes, we will. Right now, though, I want you to know Sammy is a dear old friend, and she spent some time with Chloe today."

Nigel held up his index finger up to a patron a few seats away, calming the anxious man, and turned his head a bit toward me.

"That right? She okay?" he asked, his eyes narrowing. "You a doctor?"

"No, no," Eva answered for me. "Better than that. Sammy used to work at that children's wellness center in the States that I told you about. She's here for a visit."

Nigel nodded, wearing a skeptical look. "Don't know what's so special about that place. I think Chloe needs more than a trip to the States to ride horses in some desert. We've tried everything the doctors have advised, and nothing has helped. Nothing's going to help. That's life, and it sucks." He moved down the bar, pouring and passing out more beer without a glance back at us.

Eva raised her glass. "So there's Nigel, broken by this life."

"I can feel his sadness."

FLOUNDERING IN HATE

It was a few days later when I returned to the pub alone. Nigel was bartending and I chose a stool not far from where he was standing.

He studied me for a minute. "Have we met before you came in the other day?"

"No, we haven't."

He shook his head. "Okay, I guess you just look like someone. Pint?"

I nodded. When he put the glass in front of me, I said, "Nigel. Eva has told me about your wife, and Chloe said something too."

He started scrubbing the counter. "Sammy, I don't know who you are or why you're here, and I don't need anyone else meddling in my life. What happened to Emma, and now with Chloe, well, it's just—" His blue eyes locked on mine, filling with tears. He took a few deep breaths then continued. "I don't need any more fixers in my life. Trust me, I got enough of those people. They show up to save the day, not really knowing anything about me or Chloe. They raise our hopes then nothing happens. Chloe's still sick. I still don't have a wife. I still don't have the life I used to have. I'm sick of it. And I don't need no one new coming to save the day." He moved down the bar, scrubbing away. "Don't even know if it's possible at this point."

I waited a few moments before responding. "I stopped by the hospital this morning to see Chloe. Have you been to see her recently??"

"Didn't make it over there yesterday. You think I'm a bad father because of that? I worked a 12-hour shift and just didn't . . . I just wasn't up for it." He looked much older than I knew he was.

"Nigel, I'm not here to judge you, or make you feel bad. I was just trying to make conversation. Sometimes life gets a little clearer when we can talk out our problems . . . . Tell you what . . . can you come sit with me for a few minutes? Sebastian said it was OK for you to take a break since it's not busy. He'll fix us some burgers."

Nigel glanced around, got a nod from Sebastian who was at the other end of the bar, pulled a pint for himself, then came around the bar. We took seats on either side of a nearby booth. Nigel took a big sip of his beer, scanning the bar to avoid looking at me. Finally, about half-way into his pint, he turned to me. "I'm not sure why we're here. I mean what we're going to talk about." He paused. "And I for sure thought Eva would be here, I mean with her always trying to control everything and everybody."

I raised my pint slightly. "Here's to Eva, the Queen of Control." I took a sip of beer then put down my glass. I paused, reaching across the table and took his hand. "And Nigel . . . ." He pulled away. "You do know that Eva loves Chloe, and you too."

He was quiet, sipping his pint.

"Nigel, tell me about Emma."

"I don't want to talk about it."

"OK. I understand." Silence joined us at our booth for a visit. Nigel made a trip to the men's room, then sat down and began speaking.

"I'm not sure you do understand. I'm not sure anyone does," he said. "When Emma died, so did a part of me. I know a lot of people say that, and it's true. There was something inside of me, some beautiful feeling, that I had when she was alive. And now it's gone. Just like her."

Sebastian came by to drop off two plates filled with burgers. "Need anything else?" he asked. We both nodded no.

I pick up my burger, waiting silently for Nigel to continue.

"I hate all that has happened," he continued. "I hate losing her, and not having her here with me now. I hate that Chloe is sick. I hate the nights when I get home after the pub and the house is so quiet. And I hate that I cry so much." He took another sip of beer and looked at his plate of food but didn't touch it. "And it's not fair. How's that?"

I took a deep breath, calling on the Spirit to be with me on this one. I always do this, just a little more intensely at times, and this is one of those times. "Nigel, when I said I understood, I only meant that I understood why you didn't want to talk about it. I have no basis, no past experience to understand how you feel, and how you hate. In my past life, trust me, I had my share of struggles, just nothing like yours. But I did hurt, and I did cry, and at times, at times early on, I did hate."

He looked deeply into my eyes, and stopped his pint glass on the way to his mouth in a small toasting gesture. Then he finished his beer.

He surprised me when he spoke a minute later. "Emma was one of the kindest people ever. I met her when I was 15. She was the sister of my best friend, and she would come watch our soccer games. I knew I would ask her to marry me, I just knew. When we got married, I was the happiest I'd ever been." He looked at me, a struggling smile forming below sad eyes, "And when Chloe came along, well, it was like game over for me. All I wanted to do was take care of my two ladies." He paused, folding his hands together. The anger in his voice was palpable. "It's just not fair, Sammy, just not fair. I've done everything right. I've worked hard. Was faithful to my wife. I love my little girl with everything I've got. And now I go home to an empty house that may always remain silent as a grave."

He looked at me, seemingly wanting an agreement.

"Nigel," I said, "I appreciate how hard it is for you to talk about this. I know you've had a hard time. And I want you to know I'm not here to save the day, perhaps just to help save Chloe." He teared up.

Can You Leave Hate Behind?

We ate our food, talking mostly about the pub and how he's known Sebastian for a long time. They'd worked together as carpenters. Sebastian had been his mentor before he bought the pub, and then he helped Nigel and Emma buy their house a few blocks away.

Finally, I said, "I need to be going soon but I want to say just two more things that I want you to think about."

His nod permitted me to continue. I felt I'd built some trust and had to guard that carefully. "Thank you, and know this comes from my heart. Number one, what happened to Emma is tragic. Chloe's illness is the same. Here's the thing to consider, fairness is determined by the rules of a situation, and as hard as it is to understand, or accept—and Nigel, I get it, I do—there's no rule of life that says beautiful young wives and mothers don't die, and no rule saying beautiful young daughters stay healthy. This is just life, with all of its ups and downs and with all of its shitty times."

"Yeah, shitty times indeed."

"The words we use . . . 'not fair' . . . 'hate.' These words impact us. There was a researcher who studied the impact of words on water molecules. His experiments showed human thoughts and intentions can physically alter the molecular structure of water. He claimed positive words, emotions, classical music and positive prayer directed at the water produce beautiful crystals, while negative words and emotions and crude music, produce ugly crystals, resembling water from a polluted river." He turned his head slightly in a skeptical manner. "Yes, yes, I was skeptical as well until I took a look at some of the research. And then," I pressed my finger to his chest, "I remembered our bodies are over 60% water. Interesting, right? The words we use, and how we interpret them either support us in these shitty times—" I paused, watching Nigel closely. "Or not. Nigel, I'd ask to you think about whether there's another way of looking at what you're going through. You're in a major transition in your life, perhaps the biggest you'll ever go through, and you've got to be a strong source of your own support."

I could tell he was going to protest, but closed his mouth without speaking. After a moment, he replied in a defeated tone, "I'll try."

"Nigel, don't try. Just do it; just focus on you . . . supporting you. Chloe needs her Daddy, and she needs him strong. Simply watch what you're saying to yourself about all this. The best way to change a situation is to change yourself in it."

"I'm not sure I understand."

I nodded, "Okay, let me put it this way. The little voice—sometimes not so little, and sometimes not only one—in our head, drives all that we do. It's like the pilot who's flying the plane, and is listening to the voice from the air traffic control tower. The pilot flies the plane to the place the voice tells him. It's the same with you. Your voice is flying you to the destination of your thoughts. When your little voice is talking about hate, and life sucks, and is not fair, and it's never going to get better. Well, that's the place the plane lands, the place you are now." Nigel turned his head, his eyes narrowed in thought. "I have this guy in my head who shows up from time to time. His voice is always negative, telling me how bad things are, and that they won't get better. I call him, 'ST.'"

"ST?" Nigel asked.

"Yes, it stands for shitty thoughts. ST is the voice that tells me shitty thoughts, then my pilot listens to him and lands me in a shitty place."

"But isn't it a bunch of bullshit for me to tell myself happy thoughts about the shitty times?"

"Great question, Nigel. I'm not suggesting you change the voice into one that sugar coats or ignores the facts of your situation. I believe you can support yourself by telling yourself what you see on the other side of these shitty times. Do you see you and Chloe fighting her illness, and her getting better? Do you see yourself coming to be thankful for the wonderful years with Emma, and holding happy memories from those years? Do you see yourself meeting another wonderful lady, and while you'll always hold onto your memories with Emma, you tell yourself you can create new ones with someone else?" He nodded with more understanding.

"Nigel, the voice in your head needs to tell you, that while you're in a very painful and challenging time in your life, you will get through it. Because then . . . then you'll take the right actions you need to take to do just this."

Nigel was silent, reflective, then said, "I guess it's not so much about not having the shitty thoughts, they'll come because, after all, I'm just a man. It's about not letting them win, not letting them fly the plane."

I smiled approvingly. "That's it, and this is how you can be your own source of support, in addition to Sebastian, Eva, Chloe and the others supporting you."

He nodded, breathing deeply. "You said you had two things."

"Can I show you something?" I asked, pulling my pad and pen from my bag.

He chuckled, "Oh no. Are you going to start drawing?

I laughed, "As a matter of fact, yes." I drew the transhition diagram, and talked about how there are times in our lives when we think we're living in a never-ending shit show. I then gave him the marker and asked him to draw a line through the *h*, to take the so-called shit out of the show. Nigel laughed.

"As I said before, Nigel, you're in a huge transition in life, and it's tough."

He took a deep breath, nodding and wiggling his fingers before finally resting his clasped hands on the table. "It sure is," he agreed. "I wouldn't wish this on anyone."

"No, you wouldn't." I paused. "As hard it may be to believe, this is an opportunity for you to heal and grow stronger." Nigel bit his bottom lip. "Look here," I said, pointing to the crossed-out h in transhition. "What word would you say, that begins with an h, is one that has been with you on this part of your journey. One you're now ready to leave behind."

Nigel grabbed my pen quickly and began writing on the page. He drew a capital H, then looking to me, slowly completed the word. H – A – T – E. "That's it, plain and simple, I think I need to leave behind my hate." He wiped his eyes, "I have to. It's killing me."

"That's great. Hate is an intensely charged word that is bringing negative and unproductive feelings and emotions for you."

"It sure does." Tears came and his lip quivered as I took his hand. I slid my chair around, giving him a hug, and rubbing his back.

I slid the paper in front of him, "Now scribble that word out, and think of one that you will replace it with."

Nigel stared at the paper for a minute, then quickly wrote in large letters, L-O-V-E.

"Yes." I whispered, "Tell me about it."

"I was hating everything I didn't have, things I could not control. Like losing Emma, and Chloe's sickness." He sat up taller. "If I can leave behind the hate, I can focus on everything that I still have that I can control . . . and can love." He was sobbing now, struggling to finish. "And I have Chloe, I still have Chloe. And I have to do a better job of being there for her."

We sat in quiet for some time until his breathing returned to normal. Finally, he stood and said, "I need to get back to work. But thanks for coming. You've given me a lot to think about."

Nigel and Chloe Keep Going

I didn't see Nigel again until a few days later when we both got on the same elevator at the hospital where Chloe was staying. I'd heard that he'd been spending more time with her. We exchanged greetings, then I asked if we could chat for a few minutes before going into Chloe's room. He agreed and we found some comfortable chairs in a waiting area.

"I want you . . . Eva and I want you . . . to consider getting Chloe over to that center in Utah that I know about."

He began to interrupt, but I made my voice firmer. "No Nigel, just listen. I know the Tuscany Center very well. In fact, I spent many, many years there in my life, and I know the energy of the place, the innovation of the staff there with treatment, and their intense commitment to the kids. Chloe is not responding to the treatment here. While you could wait it out here and hope something improves, I wanted to make sure that you know there's something else available. You have other choices."

Nigel began to stand up, I grabbed his arm. "Nigel, Chloe told me about your dog Winston, and that he's named after Churchill. There's a quote from Churchill I like: 'When you're going through hell, keep going.'" I let go of his arm and Nigel stood. My eyes never left his. I stood, too, and I gave him a hug, then pulled apart and asked him to look at me. "Keep going," I whispered.

* * *

After more discussions with me, Eva, Chloe, and the staff at the children's hospital, Nigel agreed to let Chloe go to Moab. They left several days later, and I followed in two weeks.

I'd not been to Moab in many years, and smiled as the red rock, sprinkled with patches of green, blended perfectly with the azure sky and puffy white clouds. The river surface was smooth, signaling the end of the melting snow, and run off from the mountains. Eva had called a few times these past two weeks, letting me know Chloe and Nigel were settled in and treatment was underway. She said Nigel seemed distant and stayed in his room most of the time.

Pulling in the parking lot of the restaurant next to the Center, I spotted Nigel sitting on one of the benches out front. White, yellow, and purple flowers spilled from the large clay pot next to the bench. He was wearing work jeans, a flannel shirt and a baseball hat supporting the colors of the Toronto FC.

"Hi, Nigel," I said as I strolled up to him.

He stood, hands in his pockets. As I stepped closer to hug him, he backed away, glancing down. "What's up?" I inquired, sliding down onto the bench. Nigel turned, staring into the foothills on the other side of the parking lot. I pushed on, "Nigel, is something going on?"

He turned quickly; his voice raised. "I'll tell you what's going on. This was not a good idea, me coming over here. I don't know anyone, and don't know my way around. My daughter is sick, they say they've got an innovative treatment that can help cure her, and yet, they can't even tell me what it is." He took a deep breath, sitting next to me, and raising his hands to his face and rubbing his temples. "I hate it," he added and smiled sarcastically at the irony.

"I'll bet there's more to it," I said calmly.

He swallowed. "I'm afraid."

I swirled my foot lightly in the gravel until he was breathing easier. "Nigel?" He did not look up. "Nigel, I understand what you're saying and how you feel. You're a long way from home, with a sick daughter in an unfamiliar place undergoing an experimental treatment. It's a lot."

"So what should I do? I feel like getting Chloe and going home today."

"Well," I began, "that's an option."

He interrupted, looking up to me. "I was talking with the mom of another sick kid. She was having a smoke when I was leaving the other day. She looked so sad, so tired, she kind of looked sick too. When I asked how things were, she stared into the distance, blew out a puff of smoke, and said, 'It's just a never-ending shitshow.' Those were almost *your* exact words, right?" I nodded.

"So, Sammy, what should I do? I was going to ring up Eva, then thought not to since she'd just yell at me."

"Well, don't worry about Eva," I said. "I'll handle her."

"Yeah, I'll say a prayer for ya on that one."

"Thanks. Maybe say some for yourself too." I winked and continued quickly, not sure of what his response may be. "In the shitshows of their lives, I've come to believe people either run away from their Faith, or to it. I'd always vote for the latter, but hey, that's just me. So, the question that seems to be dealt with is what you should do." He nodded. "Want to get a bite and see if we can figure this out?" I said, waving my thumb like a hitchhiker to the restaurant door.

He shook his head from side to side, "Nope, not much of an appetite this morning."

"OK, we can talk here. Nigel, let's put your question of what to do on the back burner for a minute, and think about another question." Nigel tilted his head slightly, squinting his eyes and holding his hands out palms up. "How about this one: What do you believe is best for Chloe?"

Nigel began to smile, "Well, shit, that's an easy one. She loves it here. The place is like Disney, and she's probably already had every flavor ice cream in that shop. She FaceTimes with Seamus and shows him all around. She loves what they call the *be still* time for the kids. It's when they go to that dark room with all the candles and just sit with that lady." I smiled, as he pulled off his hat and ran his hand through his hair. "And I guess she does look a *little* better. Her color is good, and she's not so tired. I'm just worried about this treatment and the fact that it's not really proven. It's just had some promising results."

"That's good, right?"

"Yes, I guess it is. And I really like getting to see her more, you know, not having to work and all that."

I smiled as a man with gray hair walked toward a car with two little girls, one holding each of his hands and skipping playfully. Nigel laughed when the man clumsily joined in on the skipping.

"Nigel, here's the thing, that perhaps . . . just maybe is happening for you. The human brain—your brain—likes easy and familiar, even when the familiar is sometimes not what the person says they want. I've seen it over and over with people in shitty relationships, people in poor health and eating and drinking too much, and staying in jobs where all they do is complain. Yet, they don't do anything. Why? It's hard to do the work needed to change: to make your life different. This—" I waved my hand toward the desert beyond the parking lot "—is simply just unfamiliar for you, and not so easy to get used to. And there's that part of your brain where the fight or flight response gets activated. You know, do you stick it out, so to speak, or take off."

He leaned down, retying his boot, then looked to me. "Seems I'm ready to fly out of here and get back home."

"I guess, and that's okay, remember, it's normal. The key is for you to be aware of this, and know that you have a choice. If there's one thing I've learned in life, Nigel, you always have a choice."

He stood. "I'm sorry about that time I was pissed and said I didn't need another person coming into save the day." He finished with a smile and placed an arm on my shoulder. "I'm feeling like maybe I do need some help."

"You up for a hike?"

"What?" He turned to me.

"A hike. You said you like to play soccer, and I know both your jobs are physical, so let's take a hike. It'll do you good to get that heart pumpin'." I poked his chest.

Nigel looked to the cliffs not far from us. "Here?" He asked skeptically.

"No, no, not here. Up into the mountains just a little ways from here. You can go get changed into some more comfortable clothing, have you got shorts? It'll be hot once we get going?"

"Yes, I've got a pair of soccer shorts. But I don't have any hiking shoes, or even gym shoes."

"No problem. I can scrounge up a pair for you. How about you go check in on Chloe and get changed and we'll meet at your hotel at 11:00? And be sure to eat and drink something before. I'll bring water for us."

* * *

Nigel looked more like he was ready to play soccer with Toronto FC than hike a Moab trail, the sun blindingly bouncing of his bright white shorts. His uniform-styled jersey and matching hat topped off his outfit.

"Hey Nigel." I called as my Jeep rolled to a stop in front of him. The top was down, the doors were off.

"Now this looks like fun."

He threw his backpack on the back floor and jumped in next to me. "I brought you a long sleeve shirt and borrowed a few different size hiking boots from a friend with a lot of sons," I said. "You'll need good boots for both the comfort and traction."

We pulled onto the highway; Nigel turning his hat backward as the wind in the Jeep picked up. He talked mostly about the landscape and his excitement for the hike. A wooden sign welcomed us to the parking lot that led to the trailhead. The lot was half-full, sprinkled with 4-wheel drive trucks and SUVs. Nigel read the sign out loud, "Delicate Arch Trail." He turned to me, squinting, and turning his hat around again. "This a good one?

Backing my Jeep into a spot near the top of the lot, I smiled, "Yep, you'll love it. It's just over three miles round trip with some great views."

We grabbed our gear from the Jeep. I said good morning to a young couple headed toward the trail. "We'll hike quickly to get a good workout, stopping a few times. I want you to really take all this in," I said, waving an open palm to the trail. Nigel got a pair of boots that fit well, and we began up the trail, talking causally, and stopping for some water and Nigel to take some pictures on his phone. About halfway up, I said, "Let's stop here for a bit."

A large flat rock about the size of car sat off the trail to the right, nestled next to a steep cliff. I walked to the rock, jumping on it over a small gap in the red stone, took off my pack, and sat down. Instantly the heat from the rock began to drift into my legs and butt as if sitting on a heated leather seat. I leaned back on my hands.

Nigel was standing at the edge, taking small sips from his bottle. He was gazing at red and brown land stretching until it touched the deep blue sky. "This is bloody amazing, thanks for bringing me. I needed this."

"It sure is. God did some of her finest work here, right?" He turned smiling at the use of my feminine pronoun.

"Yes, She sure did, certainly nothing about this place to hate." He chuckled, taking a seat next to me, and leaning back on his pack. He pulled off his sunglasses, looking at me seriously. "Sammy, should I be worried about Chloe's treatment? I mean, is it safe?"

"Nigel, sometimes in life, and I think this is one of those times for you, when the best thing to do is just trust. Trust is simply holding onto the belief that what you want is going to happen."

He began to smile, and chuckling said, "You know, some of our conversations remind me of Emma." Surprised a bit by his statement, I was silent. "She talked a lot about faith and trust, and the choice we all have to hold strong mindsets about life. She was always reading." He paused, kicking a pebble off the rock. "I guess you'd call them self-help books. She was always trying to get me to read one in particular called The Alchemist."

I nodded, "A classic for sure."

"This place is so beautiful, so open. I feel kind of small here. Emma would love it . . . would have loved it." He paused. "I wish she was here."

I walked past him back toward the trail, patted his shoulder and gave him a wink. "She is."

As we approached Delicate Arch, Nigel said it looked like the one on the Utah license plates, and I confirmed his observation.

At the top of the trail, people were laughing, posing for pictures, and resting. One woman sat cross-legged at the base of the arch, her eyes closed; hands resting on her knees, thumbs and middle fingers joined.

We sat on a few rocks that formed a natural table and drank some water in silence. "I'm gonna head over there a bit if that's okay." I smiled, watching Nigel navigate cracks and crevices, and taking a seat in a cluster of basketball-sized boulders. I watched as most of the people around were thumbing their phones, focused on whatever they were focused on, rather than the divine nature of their surroundings.

I laid back, closing my eyes for a few minutes of prayer. Sometime later, I opened my eyes to see Nigel sitting next to me, his forehead glistening with perspiration, and his shirt dark with sweat. He was staring out to the desert then turned to me, his bright smile contrasting with his red, wet eyes. I sat up, "You OK?"

He nodded, "You're right, Sammy, she is here." I sat up." "Emma's here for sure. I just felt her with me, I mean really felt her with me for the first time since we lost her." He was crying, drawing a look from a passing hiker. He stood, this time offering a hand to help me up, and hugged me, then let go, looking at me. "Thank you. You've helped me start realizing my strength lies in how I deal with losing Emma, and with Chloe's illness."

We slung our packs on our back and began back down the trail. "OK if I take the lead?" Nigel asked and I nodded.

"Just don't lose me." I laughed. Off we went and I noticed a lightness in Nigel. He moved quickly, turning with a smile to check on me every so often. Halfway down we made our way to an old stone bench resting about 30 yards off the trail, and sat to have a drink. The sun was still high in the sky, and the warmth felt good on my face. As we were ready to leave, the Beatles song, Let It Be, came from Nigel's pack and he grabbed his phone. "Hello." He listened. "OK, OK. I'll be there as soon as I can. Tell her I love her and it's all going to be okay." His face turned tense, his eyes on mine, shaking his head.

* * *

Several weeks later, I was walking down a street in Denver on my way to meet up with some long-time friends. Somehow, I was able to walk confidently despite wearing the new leopard print high heels that had arrived for me from Eva. I was a block from the restaurant when my phone rang.

"Hi, Nigel!"

"Sammy, hello. Is now a good time to talk?"

"Sure. I'm meeting some friends in about 15 minutes and I'd love to catch up. How's Chloe? How are you?"

"We're both good," Nigel said. "Chloe's not completely out of the woods yet and she'll likely have years of treatment ahead of her, but I think we've turned a corner. Or, maybe, it's me that has turned a corner."

"What do you mean?"

"I still have flashes of anger at times, but I'm learning to control them by focusing on my love for Emma and Chloe. I know that Emma's never coming back. I think about what she'd say to me if she was here. I can sometimes feel her presence and it helps keep me calm. And the more I focus on what I have and what I need to do to make a better life for me and Chloe, the less energy I have to think about the anger and hate that I carried for so long."

"I think it's great that you're able to both recognize your anger and hatred and also let them go. It must make Chloe happy," I said.

"I think it's helping her, too. She's always managed to put on a brave face and used to hide her anger or frustration from me because she was scared it would make me even angrier and more depressed. But now we're both being more honest with each other, so our good days are really good, and the tough days are something we help each other through."

"That's great, Nigel. I couldn't be happier about how well you're doing."

"Just one more thing, Sammy . . . I was wondering if you could do anything about getting Seamus out to Moab . . . ."

—3—

Dylan

"You never know how strong you are until being strong is the only choice you have."

– Bob Marley

Dylan on a Bridge

I hustled along the snow-covered walkway on the university campus, my hands shoved deep in my pockets and the puffs of breath looking like smoke when I exhaled. Through the glass front of the student center, I saw a large crowd milling around: some talking in groups, others in their seats, and others gathered around the food tables sitting just outside the lecture hall doors. A young man I recognized as Dylan held the door for me and I entered. He nodded slightly and said, "Good evening, ma'am. Thanks for coming tonight."

I smiled. He didn't know who I was . . . yet. "Of course," I answered. "I've been looking forward to your talk."

I slid into a chair on the aisle toward the front of the room and glanced around at the full room. The university name was on the black banner hanging at the back of the stage, the familiar buffalo logo sitting below the gold letters. Silence overtook the room as a tall man in jeans, white shirt, and black sport coat settled in front of the podium. Putting on round reading glasses, he read a poem about love and service from a Tibetan monk I'd not heard of, and then introduced the speaker, Dylan Walker, who was here to present a report on his semester abroad project conducted in Nigeria.

Dylan stepped up onto the low stage, nodding to a few of the applauding audience members. He shook the man's hand and left the podium to stand in the middle of the stage. He began, "There's a village in Nigeria, and I use the term 'village' loosely. It's just a collection of structures built from materials that most of us in this room would put out in the trash. One building is larger and more substantial, and this is where I met Dayo, an amazing young man."

Over the next forty minutes, Dylan shared the story of his trip to Nigeria, and time with Dayo and other young orphans. He told of how 40% of Nigerians—over 82 million people—lived below the poverty level on less than $382 per year. With pictures and words, he described the trash-strewn fields and streets that the people he met walked daily. He talked about the amazing people who are working to establish a school for the orphanage and how he felt he had a calling to do whatever he could to support them. His story moved the audience—and me—to laughter, tears, amazement, and discomfort.

Dylan, glanced at his watch, paused, then offered us a final thought that hung in the silence of the room, "It's almost four o'clock in the morning in Nigeria, and while many of the painfully poor people there wake to the sounds of their own growling bellies, there remains joy." As he spoke, the screen behind him filled with picture after picture of smiling people. "And that's what I learned from them. That no matter how hard life gets, there is always joy in spending time with family and friends, laughing at jokes, marveling at the natural wonders of our world. I hope we can all find that same joy. I feel very fortunate to have spent my semester abroad with these wonderful people, and I hope you will join me in supporting the schools that will provide these kids with more opportunities for joy throughout their lives." Dylan stepped off the stage as applause filled the room and people rose to their feet.

I walked to the back of the room, got a cup of tea, and watched Dylan as he worked the crowd. His height and muscular build made him resemble a quarterback talking to reporters after a game, much like his father had done years ago. After a few minutes, I moved outside and took a seat on a weathered wooden bench. Soon, clusters of people came through the doors. As the exit of people slowed down, Dylan came out by himself, pulling on a hat and gloves. He did not see me until I said his name.

"Dylan." He turned, taking a few steps toward me. "What a wonderful gift you had in spending time in Nigeria. Thanks for sharing it."

"You're welcome." He removed his glove, extending his hand. "Thank you again for coming. You obviously know how I am. What's your name?"

"Sammy."

He was a handsome young man. His face was tan, though his skin looked lighter in the areas around his eyes and across the bridge of his nose, perhaps caused by sunglasses worn regularly.

"Hi, Sammy, nice to meet. Great jacket."

I smiled, patting the faded brown leather, and pulling up the fur collar. "Keeps me warm," I said, as a young woman approached, asking Dylan if he was ready to go. "Give me a minute, Sarah?" He turned back to me. "Before I go, Sammy, what's the one thing you're taking away from tonight?"

I smiled slightly, rubbing my chin, and glancing to the lights on a foothill in the distance. "Great question, it's this: Choose joy."

"Cool," he said. "Have a good one, Sammy."

"You too," I replied. Dylan gave Sarah a one-armed hug as they set off down the lit pathway. She kissed his cheek and then hooked her arm through his as the couple walked away. While he'd seem cheerful enough during his presentation, I now noticed a hint of worry in his eyes.

* * *

One early morning the following week, I let myself embrace the rhythm of my running shoes hitting the street. Running always helped me clear my thoughts. There was no traffic as I headed away from town. The sky was clear, and the stars were just starting to fade in the brightening sky.

As I turned a corner, I caught sight of a bridge in the distance. There was a figure sitting atop the stone wall in the middle of the bridge, legs dangling down towards the river far below, arms braced. It was Dylan. He wore running gear as well. I'd expected to find him here. Dylan had contacted my boss a few weeks ago asking for help in sorting out his life. It looked like I had arrived just in time.

I stopped running and walked slowly toward him until I was a few yards away. "Dylan," I said softly. He turned quickly, tears in his eyes, and began to get off the wall.

I pulled off my hat to help him recognize me. "Wait, Dylan. It's me, Sammy. We met after the talk you gave recently."

He took a deep breath, staring down at the water rushing far below. Then he turned his head to look at me. "Yeah, I think I remember you. What do you want?"

"Just out for an early run like you." I moved closer. "Okay if I sit with you a minute?" I didn't wait for an answer, climbing onto the railing until I was seated next to him. I paused a minute then said one word. "Really?"

"Really what?"

"You thinking about jumping?"

Dylan looked at me with astonishment. "What? . . . No, no! I'm not going to jump," he said firmly. "I just like to sit here and watch the water flowing past. It helps clear my mind when my life seems to be going to hell."

"Yep, I understand. My thoughts sometimes get jumbled, too." I paused, placing my hand gently on his. "And you're right. The rushing of the water has a peace all its own even though it's constantly moving."

We remained silent for a few minutes as a truck crossed the bridge, slowing as it passed us.

"Well," I continued, "I'm starving. How about if we get down on the bridge and jog back to town. I'll buy you breakfast." He looked over, wiping his eyes with his thin running glove. "We can talk a little . . . or just eat . . . whatever you want."

Dylan took a deep breath, swung his legs, and jumped down to the road. "I guess I can do that."

Breathing a deep sigh, I offered a *thank-you* to no one in particular. I stood next to him and pulled on my hat. I tried to take his hand, but he snatched it away. "Dylan," I said, "it's all gonna be okay." He nodded slightly, his eyes looking to the other side of the bridge. "C'mon, I'll race you to the diner on 11th Street. And don't go too fast, I've been around a lot longer than you." He took off running.

As we approached the final two blocks of our run, I began to push the pace. Dylan fell behind, likely out of respect rather than a lack of conditioning. I felt strong and ran faster. With about a half of block to go, I felt Dylan close in on me, and he smiled as he cruised by. He slowed and then stopped after he passed the small, metal tables sitting empty in front of the diner. I stopped as well and bent over with my hands on my knees to catch my breath. A few moments later Dylan's running shoes appeared in my line of vision. I raised my head and saw that his face glistened with sweat. "Nice run," he said, rubbing his sleeve across his face.

A few patrons and staff moved around the diner, and we took a seat inside near the window. Dylan sipped his water, pulled at the collar of his snug running top then looked at me. "So, who are you, Sammy?"

"What do you mean?" I casually asked, sipping from my steaming mug.

"I mean, who are you, where you from, why were you at my talk, and then—" he paused, fiddling with a spoon, "and then why were you out running across that bridge the same time I was there?"

"I'm in town for just a few weeks, visiting a friend. I saw a poster for your talk on campus when I was taking a walk, and thought it would be interesting. I jog most mornings and like to take the road out of town."

He nodded. "And where you from?"

I began to answer as the waitress came. She introduced herself to Dylan, saying she was a friend of Sarah's. Dylan introduced me as a friend of his. Then she took our orders and left.

"So who's Sarah? Girlfriend?" I asked.

He stretched his neck, tilting his head from side to side. "I guess you could call her that." He paused, "I mean she is a girl, and a friend. . . . You were telling me where you're from."

"Oh, yeah. I used to live in New York a long time ago, then Utah, then LA. Now, in my semi-retirement, I travel a bunch and visit with friends, or take some trips by myself just to be alone."

Dylan nodded to a few guys coming through the front door, "You sound kind of like a mystery woman to me. No offense."

"None taken," I chuckled, "I guess that label kind of fits."

"What are your retired from? What do you do now?"

I pulled my hat off, stuffing it into the sleeve of my jacket hanging on the chair. "I did mostly financial stuff during my career, and now I do some . . . what people call life coaching."

"Got it, that kind of fits your vibe."

"Thanks," I paused, silent as the waitress put our plates on the table. "I guess."

"No, no. That's a good thing."

I winked. "I know."

We talked about the university, and that Dylan's parents had attended here. When he mentioned that his dad was a well-known former NFL quarterback, I made the appropriate comments though that was a fact I already knew. Dylan talked about growing up in Denver, and all the snowboarding he and his friends did. He said from a young age he and his sister both knew they would come to this university as well. His dad had made that very clear.

"Anything else?" the waitress asked.

"Just a refill here, please. Caffeinated," I said, sliding my mug to her. She filled it from the coffee pot she was holding. Dylan shook his head as she lifted the pot toward him. "Just the check, please," he told her.

"So, my friend Dylan—I guess we're friends now, right?" He nodded. "I have the same question she had," I said, pointing to the waitress who was now standing at the next table. Dylan squinted his eyes, tilting his head, "Anything else?" I asked.

Confronting Life's Harder Choices

Dylan surveyed the diner. He blinked his eyes, but I could tell they were getting moist. He turned to me and shook his head. "Nope. Nothing more here."

I decided to push him a little. "Dylan, at your talk last weekend, you talked about finding the joy no matter how tough life gets. It just seems to me that you're having a hard time doing that right now." And though I knew more about his situation than he realized, I didn't want to give away too much yet. "So," I said, "I don't know exactly what you're going through, but many of us have dark thoughts when we're going through life and dealing with its struggles. It's normal."

Dylan's breathing quickened as he shifted in his chair. "Can we go?" he asked, standing and putting on his jacket.

"Sure." I pulled some bills from my pocket and placed them below the check on the table.

Outside, he made a left, and then another, leading me down a narrow alley where brick walls rose several stories high on each side. We popped out the other side of the alley onto a pedestrian mall, filled with statues and fountains and weathered wooden benches. He eventually dropped down onto one of the sturdy benches and looked across the mall to the mountains in the distance. Taking a place next to him, I followed his gaze to the mountains.

"Sammy," he said, his eyes not moving, "I can't believe I'm gonna talk to you about what's going on." He laughed. "I only told one person about what all is going on —that's my friend Sarah. You may have seen her at the talk you came to. Never thought the next person I'd tell would be some lady I met just a week ago."

"Sometimes," I said, "it's easier to talk to a stranger about important issues than people who are close to you." I smiled and nodded to encourage him to keep talking.

"Everything in my life on the outside looks great. I'm about to graduate. I found a purpose in life thanks to my semester abroad in Nigeria. I've lived a life of privilege because of my dad. But inside is another story. I've got a lot I need to work out." He paused. "And if I don't—well, I don't know what will happen but maybe I could be on that bridge someday thinking about what you thought I was going to do." He looked at me, sadness in his eyes. "You said it's all gonna be okay, and I wish I could believe that. It's just that right now . . . inside me . . . it's one big shitshow." He bit his lip, fighting back tears. "And I am really freakin' confused."

A young man on a mountain bike, covered in ski gear, pedaled quickly across the mall. Dylan watched his progress for a few seconds then looked to me.

"Yes. I get it. I guess it's a coincidence we met, or maybe not, I don't believe in them. What matters is that you know this shitshow that is playing out within you—it does not need to win." He looked to me, listening intently. "There are many reasons it can; and many reasons it won't. And just like your friends in Nigeria, it comes down to a choice; to your choice about how you're going to deal with your situation."

"Yeah, right. I hear that word 'choice' a lot lately. I'm not sure that's true." He paused. "Sammy, I'm gay. And trust me, I finally realized I don't have a choice in the matter."

I looked deeply into his eyes and reached out to place my hand on his leg. No words would be the right ones, so I just turned my gaze to the mountains.

"I know that for a lot of people—a lot of my friends actually—coming out about being gay isn't a big deal. But it will be for me."

Dylan's phone pinged and he checked the message. "Sorry, Sammy, but I've got to go." He turned and started walking away.

"Wait just a second, Dylan," I called to him. "I'd really like to hear more about what's going on with you. Could we meet again tonight or tomorrow to talk."

He turned but didn't look excited about my suggestion.

"Listen, I don't have all the answers," I said. "And I wouldn't give them to you if I did. You have to figure out what's going to be best for you . . . . But how about this. How about for now, just today, you begin to think about what choices you *do* have . . . and I mean all the choices. What can you choose to do—or not to do— in dealing with something that's going on in your life?"

Dylan didn't speak for a few moments, then said, "I think I can do that."

I handed Dylan *my* phone, asking him to call *his* phone so he would have my number and I would have his. "I'm free for dinner tonight . . . breakfast tomorrow . . . or any time you want to talk. I'm here for another week or so, and I'd like to talk to you more after you've thought about your choices . . . That is, if you're willing. I have a lot of free time."

Dylan said he'd like that. I gave him a hug and walked toward the rising sun.

Later that day, after a wonderful hike where the blue sky seemed to stretch on forever and a lone eagle flew overhead, I received a text.

> Dylan: hey sammy, this is Dylan. our talk got me thinking
> . . . a lot. Can you meet me and Sarah for dinner?
> Tacos? Maybe a margarita? I can probably use one.

Me: absolutely. where? when?

Dylan: rio grande, just off the mall, on the roof, 5:00 OK? Wednesday nights get busy, "hump day" right?

Approaching the restaurant just off the mall, I heard my name from above, "Sammy, Sammy." Glancing up, I saw Dylan leaning out over the iron railing atop the stone restaurant on the corner, and waving his arm to come up. I made my way through a crowd of people nestled between the bar and a few booths. A stairway hung along the white brick wall in the back, and I figured that was my route. Dylan was at the top of the steps, welcoming me with a smile and hug. I followed him to the table where I recognized Sarah from the night of Dylan's talk. "Sammy, this is Sarah. You met her briefly at my talk."

Sarah stood and, ignoring my outstretched hand, wrapped her arms around me. She squeezed me tight, her broad shoulders firm and muscular. We parted, and she looked at me with dark eyes sitting under the brim of her baseball hat with the word Aspen across the front. "Sammy, I don't know where you came from, but I'm sure glad you're here." We all sat, the waiter welcoming me and clearing some empty salt-rimmed glasses, the limes sitting in the melting ice. "How about a margarita, Sammy?" asked Sarah, holding up an almost-full glass. "They're really good."

"Sure," I said, smiling at the waiter.

"You ever been here before?" Sarah asked.

"No, and I think I'm going to like it. I saw some food on tables on the way up and it looks really good."

"It is for sure," Dylan offered. "And the margs are just the best." He swirled his glass, "Liquid courage." He raised his glass to Sarah, who clinked hers to his as the waiter dropped a napkin in front of me, placing the glass on it. "To liquid courage." Dylan toasted as we all three raised our glasses. I took a sip, peering over my glass to Sarah, then Dylan. I placed my glass back on the wet circle on the napkin.

When the waiter was done taking our order, I asked, "So, what's up? Why did you ask me to dinner? And what's all this liquid courage stuff? I think I know what that means . . . I used it a lot when I was working on Wall Street a lifetime ago. If I remember correctly, I'm not sure it really served me well. I'd usually wake with a new hangover, but the same old problem."

Dylan looked to Sarah, then his eyes settled on mine. "I spent the day thinking about my choices, like you asked me to do. As it turns out, my dad always hosts a huge tailgate party right before the big spring intrasquad football game, which happens to be this Saturday. He and my mom and sister are driving up for the weekend. They always arrive on the Thursday before the game so I'm going meet up with them tomorrow night . . . and I've decided I'm going to tell them I'm gay."

I sipped my marg. "So they don't know?" Dylan glanced to Sarah, who was shaking her head. "I see. OK, anything I can do to support you?"

"No, not really," he said. "I've known this day would come, and Sarah has been unbelievable in helping me, and talking with me and crying with me. I just have to do it. This hiding . . . this pretending, is killing me." He took a very deep breath and sat up in his chair. "Well, it hasn't yet, but close."

"It'll be okay." Sarah said, as laughter erupted from a group of students at a corner table.

We all looked to them. Dylan said, "Yeah, it would be nice to have something to laugh about. Just don't think there's gonna be a lot of smiles and laughter in my life any time soon."

"What are you expecting?" I asked.

"Well, I'm thinking my mom will cry and hug me. She won't approve but won't turn me away. My sister, well, not sure there." He stopped talking, finished his margarita and stared into the empty glass.

"And your dad?"

"Yeah, him. Well, Sammy, let me tell you a little about him, and then you can make your prediction. My dad is from a very Catholic family. He's involved with the church in Denver, and as a matter of fact is real good friends with the Archbishop of Denver. Believe it or not, the archbishop played in the NFL for a few years with my dad. After his playing career, my dad built a very successful real estate and construction company."

I nodded slowly, "OK, I get it . . . I think."

He continued, "My dad and I are . . . or at least were very close for most of my life. He taught me to throw a football and he and Mom have come to every game I played since I was in grade school. We spent a lot of time together when I was growing up—working in the garage, hunting and fishing, and talking about sports.

"Looking back, I guess you could say that I spent a lot of my youth having my dad teach me how to be what he'd call a 'man's man.' He thinks the Church is going too far in accepting gay people, even if they don't act on their impulses, as he puts it. He once told me that a protest group had put up a gay pride flag on a construction site and he had one of his crew burn it. And the icing on the cake is that I played football here my first two years, and did OK. He and my mom came to every game, home and away."

"And . . ."

"And I retired, so to speak. My heart was not in it. I wasn't playing for me anymore." He smiled, looked to Sarah, and tapped her hat brim. "I haven't played for me in a long time."

"I'm guessing your Dad—what's his name?"

"Eric."

"I'm guessing Eric is not so happy about this . . . and probably won't be happy about your announcement."

"You guessed right. Get this," he said with a short laugh, "just last week he handed me a beautiful ring. He said it had been his grand-mother's and he wanted me to use it when I proposed to Sarah. He thinks that since I've given up football and am about to graduate, it's time for me to settle down, get a job, get married, and have babies. He wasn't really wild about my plan to go back to Nigeria."

I was about to respond when Sarah interrupted. "Sammy, the night you met Dylan after his talk, he told me he felt like he knew you from somewhere. He said it was a weird feeling." She looked at Dylan, who took a deep breath and nodded my way. "He told me about the bridge this morning, and the weird way you just showed up, and the talk you guys had."

Her eyes filled with tears, as she reached to place her hand in Dylan's. "This guy is my best friend." She looked to him, then back to me. "I'd marry him in a minute," she laughed, wiping the tear running down her cheek. "But I guess that really wouldn't work out now, would it?" Dylan gave her a wink and squeezed her hand.

"So how can I help you, Dylan?" I asked.

"Sammy, could you come to the tailgate?"

"I wouldn't miss it," I said.

Get Out the Shovel

I was getting ready for bed on Thursday night when my phone buzzed. The caller ID indicated it was Sarah, so I quickly answered.

"Hey, Sarah, everything OK? I was hoping I'd hear from you or Dylan," I said, doing my best to not sound overly concerned.

"Dylan talked to his family tonight as planned and now he's a mess. His mom cried. His sister said, 'about time you came out. I knew all along.' And his dad just sat there, shaking his head, then stalked out of the hotel room without saying a word to Dylan. Can you text him? He's not doing real good."

I quickly agreed, texted Dylan, and got an "I'm OK" text in response. I texted back asking him to meet me at the bridge for a run at 8am tomorrow morning and I'd treat him to breakfast again afterwards. He didn't reply.

Time crept along as it does when all you want is to support someone, to be with them, to search for the right things to say, and they don't let you. I knew Dylan is on his own journey, like all of us. It's just that during shitty times too many people go it alone . . . when they're anything but alone.

The sun was chasing the chill from the air the next morning as I walked toward the bridge. The clear sky went on forever. Ever the optimist, I stood at the spot where Dylan had been sitting on the bridge railing, stretching for my body to wake up, for it has many, many miles on it. Eight o'clock came and went, and it was closer to nine o'clock when I started to pull out my phone to text Dylan. That's when I saw him shuffling my way. His shoelaces dragged along the bricks; his hair was in dire need of a comb. He shook his head as he approached, "Sorry

I'm late, Sammy." He moved in for a hug and I caught smell of the reason for his tardiness.

"Whew!" I said, opening my eyes wide. "I think I'm a little drunk just from that hug."

He smiled sadly. "Yeah, sorry again. Rough night, way too many shots. I suppose Sarah told you what happened last night."

I nodded.

"I'm guessing you probably want to grab me by the collar and shake the shit out of me," he continued.

I took a deep breath, smiling and laughing lightly as I exhaled. "Dylan, I'm a peaceful Soul, and I have to say, that thought has crossed my mind." I hit him on the arm playfully, "Don't beat yourself up. I'm surprised you got here this early. Come on, let's forget the run this morning. I'll buy you a cup of coffee at the diner if you're not up for breakfast."

I turned and began walking away, but stopped as he grabbed my arm. "Sammy, wait. I am sorry, really. Again, it's weird how you showed up, and are here with me at this time in my life, this shitty time. You're supporting me, and I do this. I should have known that getting drunk doesn't change anything."

I took his arm, like an escort walking into a ballroom, and started heading toward the diner. "Getting drunk usually seems like a good idea at the time. But you're right, all it really provides the next day is a new hangover and the same old shitshow." I paused and looked at him closely. "Have you reached a point where it's time to bring out the shovel and get some of the shit out of your life?"

He nodded.

I continued, "I know you were originally planning to go to the tailgate before the spring football game tomorrow. You still going?"

"I'm not sure. I think I have to. But I'm not sure how I'm gonna handle this. Any suggestions?"

I shook my head slowly. "This is your call my friend. Your call. I'm here to support you as best I can. What have you done in the past when you first see your dad at the tailgate?"

He wiped his eyes, turning to me. "We hug."

I didn't react. He walked a few more steps then said, "And that's what I'll do tomorrow. I'll give him a hug." I nodded, "It's not like I'm gonna be running and jumping from Winnebago to Winnebago waving a rainbow flag, right? I'm just giving my Dad a hug."

"That's right," I said. "But I do have one tip for you. Don't focus on what you think your dad is going to do. Stay focused on *your* choices . . . how you are going to act no matter what your dad says, or does, or doesn't do."

"I just wish I knew what he was thinking. I wish I knew what he was gonna do. My mom called me this morning, otherwise I probably wouldn't have woken up so early. She said Dad told her he won't accept this." He stared right through me. "Hearing that makes me realize he won't accept *me*."

"Come with me," I grabbed him by the arm, leading him to a nearby bench. "You've had a rough couple of days that were the culmination of a lot of turmoil in your life. I think you called your life a shitshow yesterday. And that's what it is. At least at this moment."

I went on to explain that shitshows are really just transitions. Transitions filled with chaos, stress, uncertainty, fear, regret, and a long list of many other negative, potentially defeating forces. A person needs to move from one place to another, at least philosophically. They need to move their life, their current state, to another one . . . a more desirable, graceful one.

"Our shitshows are the difficult transitions of our life," I said. "The other transitions are our happy times—getting married, becoming parents, starting new jobs, moving to a new home." He nodded and began to speak but I raised my hand to cut him off. "I want you to think about this. If you put the letter 'h' after the 's' in the word transition, what would it spell?"

He looked confused, "What are you talking about?" He reached down, pulling at the top of his shoe and finally tying the laces. "I guess you'd have the word, tran-shit-shun." He sat up and laughed, "Is that really a word?"

"It is now, and you're in one. What you have to think about doing is simply removing the 'h' so you can turn your 'transhition' into a transition that leads you to a better place."

He nodded, twirling his index finger in the air to keep me talking.

"So, here's one way that helps a lot of people take that control. Think about a word that describes you now, maybe something you're doing now, that begins with an 'h'; a word that is keeping you from moving on, and through, this time to a better place."

"I'm not sure."

"Yes, you are. You told me if you didn't stop this it would kill you."

Dylan sat still, his mind racing, then turning to me, tears in his eyes. "Hiding."

I pursed my lips, my eyes on his. After a minute, I whispered, "That sounds about right. . . . Now think about what word or phrase you want to describe where you're going—the state of mind you want to have from this moment forward."

Dylan thought for a few moments then finally said, "Courage. I want to be courageous and live my life with authenticity. I know that's a buzzword lately but it's what I want . . . to be my real self all the time."

"I think that's a great word," I said. "So, by taking the 'h' of 'hiding' out of your tran-shit-ion, you can *transition* to a life with more courage: with more authenticity. You've already taken the first step of this new journey. Now it's time to keep moving forward."

Just Be Dylan

The next day, I walked across the parking lot toward the corner closest to the massive stadium. Motor homes, campers, pick-up trucks, and every other vehicle you can think of were jammed into the lot like a puzzle with a few extra pieces. The smell of barbeque invaded the air. Music played, and people tossing bean bags into round holes on slanted boards were abundant. It was a human sea of black, gold, and white.

Approaching the corner, I noticed the motor home that must be the Walker's. It was black, shining like patent leather shoes on a wedding day, with a large gold logo painted on the side, and an awning hanging off its side. It was the only vehicle angled into the corner, offering it a commanding view of the lot. I felt a hug from behind, turning to see it was Sarah, a buffalo sticker on her cheek.

"Hey Sammy, how about this weather? Perfect, right?"

"Sure is."

Her expression turned serious. "Did you talk with Dylan this morning?" she whispered.

"Yes, I did. I hope I helped him a little. Is he here yet?"

"No, any minute, I guess. Here, let me introduce you to his mom and sister."

Sarah took my hand and lead me to a woman dressed in jeans, black sneakers, and a gold athletic pullover. The woman was standing near a portable bar topped with bottles, cups, and trays of cut fruit; two young women were talking next to her. She saw Sarah and placed her cup on the bar. "Sarah!" She extended her arms, a look of sadness on her face. "So glad you're here. Is Dylan with you?"

"No, he should be here soon."

Sarah turned to me. "Mrs. W, this is our friend, Sammy. She met Dylan after the talk he did about the orphanage."

I extended my hand and we shook. I couldn't help but notice the subtle dark circles under her eyes showing through her layer of makeup. "Hi Sammy," the woman said. "Becca Walker, nice to meet you."

"You too, Becca. You've got a fine son." Her eyes narrowed, as she glanced from me to Sarah, seeking to know if I knew. "And yes, I know what's going on." I was introduced to Dylan's sister and her friend, and Sarah moved away with them, fixing herself a drink.

I turned as I heard Dylan's voice calling to us. He went right to his mom, embracing her in a long hug. She pulled away, her hand quickly wiping a tear. He turned to me and we hugged. "So, I see you met," he said.

"Yes, I was just going to ask her how you two met. Funny you never mentioned her to me before."

Dylan's chest and shoulders raised, taking in a deep breath, and smiling as he let it out his nose. "Mom, can we talk about this later? Where's Dad?"

She nodded, saying nothing, and moving to engage with Dylan's sister and friend. Dylan gave his sister a quick hug from behind, kissing her cheek. "Hey D." She said, smiling over her shoulder. "You good?"

"Hanging, just hanging." She gave him a wink, smiled, and turned away.

Dylan scanned the people around the massive black RV, settling on two men about twenty feet away. "Look, there he is, the legendary Eric Walker." I turned to see two men, one facing us and the other with his back to us. They appeared to be in their mid-forties with athletic builds, and both wearing university athletic attire where they could have passed for coaches.

"Which one?" I asked.

Dylan laughed sarcastically, "The one with his back to us, and the outline of the sharpie pen in his back pocket." I looked to them, the man facing us making eye contact with me. "The other is Archbishop Michael Trumball. He's the archbishop of Denver I told you about, and a good friend of my dad's. Believe it or not, Archbishop Trumball was an all-American in college, and played in the NFL for a few seasons. That's how they became friends."

"Wow." I chuckled, "interesting career path." Dylan tilted his, nodding slightly.

"Do you think your father told him?"

"100%"

We both looked to see the archbishop smile and give a wave, and reading his lips when he said, "Dylan's here." Dylan's dad did not turn.

"Shit. Shit, Sammy, this sucks. He can't even turn around. I feel like leaving." He breathed deeply. "What should I do?"

"Your call, my friend. Remember what we talked about yesterday morning. You can take some of the 'h' out of your show right now by walking over there and giving him the hug you told me about."

"But what if he doesn't return it?" he asked, plunging his hand deep in his pockets.

"That's *his* choice. Right now, you have a choice where you can move from hiding to courage. That was your word: courage . . . the act of doing something that scares us." He looked up to me, staring deeply into my eyes. "Dylan, there are some people that will not accept you, and your Dad may be one of them, as sad as this is. And there are others who will; and I'm sure Dayo, and the rest of those wonderful children at the orphanage will."

"I guess you're right," he said.

"Dylan, it's not at all about me being right. It's about you doing what you believe—in here"—I poked his chest—"what you believe in here is right."

"Will you come with me?" I nodded.

The archbishop saw us but didn't say anything to Eric. Dylan stopped a few feet from his father's back. "Hi, Dad." His father turned slowly, his face expressionless, eyes hidden behind aviator sunglasses. Dylan moved in for a hug. Eric held his cup way from Dylan, his arms not closing around his son. Just then three young boys, dressed from hat to shoes in school gear yelled, "Mr. Walker, Mr. Walker, will you sign my jersey?"

The other said, "No, mine first." Eric Walker turned from his only son, smiling, and signing the boy's jersey's then taking the small football from one and throwing it back to him as the boys ran away. He turned, finished his drink and walked back towards where Dylan's mom was standing at the bar.

The archbishop smiled sadly, moving in and hugging Dylan tightly. They separated, the archbishop remaining close to Dylan.

"I suppose my dad told you what's going on?" asked Dylan.

"Yes, he did, Dylan. How are you?" replied the archbishop.

Dylan looked stunned for a brief moment, like he wasn't expecting such a civil response from the archbishop.

"I'm struggling," Dylan said at last. "In fact, I was hoping I could make an appointment to talk with you about . . . well, about everything. What's happening with me. My plans for the future and the grant I was hoping to get for another trip to Nigeria. Would that be possible?"

"I think that's a great idea, Dylan. I agree that we have a lot to talk over. Come by my office any time this next week."

Dylan gave a slight smile. "Great. I'll call your office on Monday, and make an appointment." He walked off.

Sarah and I mingled with the crowd for about an hour, my eyes always scanning for any sign of Dylan. None. We both texted him, and he said he was over in another lot with some friends. The game was beginning, so I bid farewell to Sarah, telling her there was a book and porch chair with my name on it. We agreed to stay in touch, and see one another tomorrow with Dylan. When I arrived on my porch, I sent a quick text to Dylan.

> Me: Hey. Proud of you. it took courage. You should be proud of yourself. Stay in touch if you need anything. And remember, "new hangover" not the way to go luv ya 😀

I began reading, then stopped, thinking it better to check in with my boss. The days of the week and times of the day meant nothing to us in terms of our communication. We talked whenever needed. I provided a quick update on Dylan, expressed my concern, and as I always do, asked for guidance. My phone buzzed just as I finished:

> Dylan: thanks, luv ya back. Breakfast tomorrow? Diner. 7am. I'll be sober.

> Me: You're on.

* * *

The next morning, Dylan and I rehashed his meeting with his dad. He didn't see much hope there, and was optimistic that his meeting with the Archbishop would mean he could continue with his immediate plans.

"While you're meeting with the Archbishop, I want to you to hold onto the image of the bridge," I said.

Dylan's eyes showed concern. "The bridge?" he asked hesitantly. "Why do you want me to envision the bridge? I'd think you'd want me to forget about that."

"Yes, I know. Perhaps see that bridge, just think about it differently. Don't focus on it as something that is crossing some hypnotic waters far below. Rather, see that bridge as the path to get from one part of your life to another. To a new, better, part."

He remained silent, wiping the tears from his eyes.

"One thing I know for sure," I continued, "is the only person you can control, or change is yourself. And trust me, that's the only person you want to. It gets really messy when you try to do it to others. I guess what I'd offer you is don't worry about your dad, and what he's going to do, or how he's going to be. He's on his own journey, and he'll either figure this out . . . or not. There's a quote I love from St. Francis de Sales, 'Be who you are and be that well.'"

Dylan nodded, looking away. I reached out, gently turning his face to mine. "Just be Dylan."

—4—

Jill

"The highest tribute to the dead is not grief but gratitude."

— Thornton Wilder

Jill in a Rage

I was waiting outside my hotel, enjoying the beauty of Florida's Gulf Coast in this small town nestled on the coast of the clear waters. My boss and I had spoken the other day about my newest client, Jill, one of my seven. It seems a friend of hers, a woman from their church named Martha, was asking if my boss would please send someone to help. My boss said I should use Martha's name when I met Jill's husband, Arjun.

As I do sometimes, I'll research the client through social media or Google to see what I can find out. Arjun's social media page showed a man of about 35 or 40 smiling in the driver's seat of a black convertible Porsche; a young boy sat in the passenger seat wearing a matching smile.

I immediately recognized that car when it pulled into the driveway that led up to the hotel. I waved at the driver who stopped in front of me then got out of the Porsche.

"You must be Sammy," he said with a strong Indian accent. He was shorter than me, his bright blue eyes contrasting with his dark skin. His jet-black hair was thick and short, and his round head and chubby face sat on his equally round body.

I took his hand, "I am Arjun. It is my pleasure to meet you."

"It is very nice you have come, and agreed to meet," he replied. "I did not recognize the text I received about meeting with you, although it made sense since I had talked with Martha at church, and she said she was asking about someone to help me—." He paused, then continued. "And Jill, my wife too. If it's OK with you, I'll take us right to the house. It's about a 20-minute drive and we can talk on the way."

As we drove, I kept silent, letting the beauty of the day and the environment wash over me. Palm trees rose high against a solid blue sky while herons and flamingos stood and swooped along the roadside waters.

After a few minutes, Arjun spoke. “I don’t know where to begin,” he said, keeping his eyes on the road. “I have been thinking about this a long time, and now, I am at a loss.” I noticed a small glass prism hanging from the rearview mirror, and held it lightly in my fingers. Arjun smiled.

“It is my son’s,” he said. “Or I guess I should say it was my son’s. He gave it to me when I first got the car. We used to take so many rides in it, and then when he was old enough, he would drive. We had a deal that I would give this car to him, and he would then give it to his son.”

I let the prism go. The light bounced off and through it, shimmering across our legs and the car interior as it swayed back and forth. “Arjun. I am sad for you for your loss of Andrik. I know your pain is great, and you miss him dearly.”

“Yes, I thought you would know. From Martha, or some way.” He pursed his lips, seemingly pushing back tears. “Sammy, we need your help, someone’s help. I think I can be okay. I am sad: very, very sad, yet I am moving on.” He paused. “My wife, Jill, though, well, I am very worried about her. It has been over two years now, and she . . .” his voice drifted off. A moment later he finished. “Well, you will see.”

Not long after we pulled to the curb in front of a large home, the finely manicured lawn flowing to trimmed bushes and flowers all around. As we followed the brick walk to the double front door, I noticed the curtains of a second-floor window pull back briefly, then close. Arjun opened the door and we entered.

The foyer opened up to a second floor and the rooms were very open, blending into one another and separated only by the color of the walls. Dark hardwood floors spilled throughout the home, with bold white columns scattered throughout.

"Your home is lovely," I said.

"Thank you." He said glancing to the staircase quickly, then walked toward the kitchen. "Here, let's head to the kitchen. Would like some coffee, tea, or something? I have a wonderful Indian tea that is said to bring peace and calm to the person enjoying it."

I took a seat on a strong wooden stool at the counter, "That sounds perfect. I can always use some peace."

Arjun began opening cabinets, and moving pots, doing so with very little sound. He took a seat , placing a delicate cup in front of me, smelling of herbs with a hint of citrus. "Thank you."

We sat in silence, sipping our tea, then Arjun turned, "Sammy. I am sorry. Jill will not see you. We spoke this morning, and she said there is nothing some strange woman who does not know her, or did not know her son, can do or say to make things better." He looked to his tea, "I thought just maybe, maybe she would come downstairs when she heard us. I am sorry."

"There's no need for sorry, Arjun. I understand. And it's all going to be okay. . . . This tea is wonderful, what is it?"

"It is a tea my cousin makes; she lives not far from here." He said, his Indian accent still reaching a pitch even through his effort to remain quiet. "It is called shaanti."

"Shaanti?"

"Yes, this is our Indian word for peace."

"Shaanti, nice."

"Sammy, I asked Martha about you because Jill wanted to know who you were, and why you showed up." I nodded. "Martha said she did not know you, although she did say she had mentioned all of this to another woman at church, and perhaps she is the one who knows your boss."

"I'm not certain, Arjun, although that sounds right." He stood, moving to the other side of the island.

A door slammed behind us, causing us to turn. A woman in black sweatpants and a hoodie with a soccer ball and the words *Stone Hill Prep* across the front walked deliberately toward us. Her auburn hair was pulled back with a gray headband, dirty and disheveled, and subtle darkness sat beneath the cold, dark eyes of her pale face.

She strode right to Arjun, her voice stern and loud. "Why is she here? I told you I didn't want to see this, this stranger. I told you we do not need some lady here to help us. She does not know us." She turned to me. "And we do not know her. You should leave. Now." Her arms were at her side, her fists clenched. I stood.

"Jill, honey," Arjun began, before she interrupted. His effort to grab her was useless, as she took a quick step back.

"Do not . . . Do not 'honey' me," she said through clenched lips.

I knew this woman was hurting, and had expected to experience it, although her intensity was stronger than I'd ever seen in a grieving parent, especially after a few years. I took a deep breath, calling on the Spirit, and pushed my chair back.

"I should be going."

"Yes, you should. And no need to come back." Jill was shaking. "Who the hell do you think you are? Showing up here with your pretty gray ponytail? You have no idea what is going on here." Her stare was fixed strongly on me.

"Jill, I under . . ."

"Lady, you don't understand shit. Nothing. Now get the hell out of here."

Arjun went to hug Jill, and again was thwarted as she crossed her arms, stormed through the back door, and walked toward the diving board end of the pool.

I looked to him, nodding as I smiled softly, and walked around the side of the house, following the brick walkway that led through a gate and out to the driveway. Arjun followed me.

"I will give you a ride back to your hotel," he said.

I put my hand on his arm. "I'd appreciate that, Arjun. And trust me, Jill is going to be okay."

PAIN LIKE NOTHING ELSE

As expected, Arjun texted me that evening.

> Arjun: Thanks for coming to the house today. Sorry Jill was so angry and rude. We fought and I said some things that made her angrier. If you are open to it, I would like to meet again with you. I need help.

> Me: No sorry needed. I understand Jill and her anger, and do not take it personally. Yes, let's meet. When and where.

> Arjun: How about the park by my house tomorrow at sunrise if that's not too early? I'll bring coffee and bagels.

> Me: Perfect. See you then

> Me: And maybe go sit by the pool or take a drive and just breathe. As I said a few times, it's all gonna be okay

> Arjun: I'm not so sure about that

The next morning, I drove my Jeep to the park, laced up my running shoes, and pulled on a light jacket to push off the cool air left over from the night. The sun was barely showing through some trees on the horizon. I spotted Arjun's Porsche right away and saw him on a swing not far from a picnic table. I walked toward him, and called his name. "Good morning, Arjun."

He got off the swing, turned his sad face my way then walked over to meet me, leaving footprints on the wet grass. We hugged. "Good morning, Sammy," he said. "Thanks for meeting. Looks like you're dressed for a run. I should take a page from your book and begin exercising more." He patted his little belly. "Let me get our coffee and food."

Arjun retrieved several towels and a few large bags from his car. We used the towels to dry the table and benches, then Arjun brought out the coffee, bagels, a bowl of fruit, and several utensils. The aroma of coffee filled the air as we both sipped from our cups, then scooped cut fruit into small bowls and spread toppings over our bagels. The sun began to warm the park, as mist began rising off the dew-covered grass.

Arjun was facing the rising sun, it's light sparkling in his turquoise eyes as he glanced over my shoulder. "When we met yesterday, you kept saying to me 'it's all gonna be okay' over and over. Why do you say that??" He took a bite of his bagel, a smidge of cream cheese sticking to his lip until he got it.

Taking a sip of coffee, I nodded, smiling, "Yeah, that. If I had a dollar for every time I got this question . . . well, I pointed my coffee cup toward his car, I could buy you another one of those." Arjun smiled slightly, his eyes calling for the answer to his question.

"Arjun, here's the thing about being okay with something, even the tragic loss of Andrik. The definition of okay is . . . "

He interrupted. "My son's name, Andrik, means 'the sun rising between the mountains.'" He smiled, pointing to the sun with his finger while holding a final bite of bagel. "This is why I love the sunrise. It reminds me of him. I know this may sound crazy, after Andrik passed away, I would wash my car at sunrise. I could feel him, his Spirit."

"Doesn't sound crazy to me, knowing how much Andrik loved that car." I paused. "And you and Jill."

Tears filled Arjun's eyes, "Well . . . right after Andrik died, I washed the car every other day. I'd pull it out of the garage, wash it, and pull it back in. For months this went on. I got some stares from the neighbors for sure. Crazy, right?"

I reached across the table, taking Arjun's hand. "Not crazy at all. Sometimes, we just have our own way of getting us through life's tough times." He smiled, sniffling, and wiped his nose with his sleeve. "I bet the car was pretty clean, though?" I pushed his hand away playfully.

"Never cleaner." I noticed a car pull quickly into the lot, parking next to Arjun's. He turned at the sound, as Jill got out of the car, slamming the door with all the violence she could muster, and charging our way in the same clothes she was wearing at the house.

We both stood. She pushed Arjun, "You son of a bitch. First, I lose my son, then I lose my husband, to this cute little sunrise breakfast." Arjun began to talk, and she continued, cutting him off. "And you," she came to me, her face just inches from mine, "Why don't you just jump back on whatever cloud it is you floated in on and get the hell out of here."

Arjun grabbed her from behind, spinning her strongly to face him. "Jill, you stop this, right now." His voice was loud, his face red, and his hands clasped her wrists. "You say 'First I lose my son' . . . well, Andrik was not just *your* son, he was mine too." Tears came and his voice broke. "And losing your husband? Jill, this is not the case. It's the other way around. I lost my wife. You didn't lose me, I'm right here, I lost you dammit."

Jill struggled to get free. A man jogging near the swings saw what was happening and changed his course to come our way. I raised my hands as if to communicate that it was alright. He slowed, walking backward to his path for a minute.

"I lost you." Arjun whispered.

Jill stared into Arjun's eyes. He loosened his grip and she collapsed to her knees, sobbing out all the pain inside her. Arjun fell to his knees, wrapping his wife in his arms and rocking her gently. A few minutes passed as Jill's sobs became gradually softer and less frequent. Arjun stood, bringing Jill along by her hands, the knees of his pants wet from the grass, and the front of his shirt stained with tears and snot.

She sat down on the picnic table bench, took a few deep breaths, and wiped her face with a napkin from the table. "Would you like some coffee?" I asked, grabbing a cup. She nodded, her face void of expression.

"And a splash of cream, no sugar," Arjun added, his thumb caressing her hand, and other arm around her shoulder as he sat beside her. I handed the cup to Jill, who closed her eyes and wrapped the cup in both hands to welcome the warmth. Jill sipped her coffee as Arjun gave me a look of concern. I knew from experience to let silence do all the talking for a while.

Jill looked to Arjun, then to me. "Sammy . . . that is your name?"

"Yes."

"Sammy. Do you have children?"

"Yes, one."

"Then you know that joy, that one-of-a-kind joy that occurs when we give birth to our child. And that little pink, smooth-faced baby is laid in your arms. Placed on your chest." Jill began to look away as she said this.

"I'm afraid I don't." She turned her head slightly. "My son, Noah, is adopted." A look of surprise crossed her face. "It's okay."

"I see," Jill responded with the calculating tone of an attorney in a courtroom. "Do you ever wish you had a biological child? Did you ever imagine what it would be like to have your child inside you? To actually be one with another person?"

"Jill, that's a personal question," Arjun said in a scolding tone.

"Oh, is it? Well, we all seem like we're getting more personal here. I mean breakfast at sunrise, come on." Turning from Arjun to me, Jill apologized, her voice oozing sarcasm. "I'm so, so sorry Sammy."

"No, no, all good. I understand. My friends have told me *bearing a child* is the most intense pain; I disagree. You are in the most intense pain of having *buried your child*. Jill, I have felt joy in being a mother, and I can only imagine the even more intense joy you talk about, when a mother carries a child in her womb, and then gets the gift of bringing their child into this world." My eyes remained on hers; I was determined to get a breakthrough with this woman, no matter how small.

Jill's eyes filled as she said adamantly, "No Sammy, I don't believe you can."

Jill rose to leave, and I took her hand. She began to pull away; I tightened my grip, squishing her fingers and causing a grimace as she sat back down. Arjun was still. "Jill, you believe what you want. My love for my son, my adopted son, Noah, is as intense a love as I know." I paused, pulling her hand closer across the table.

"And since we're sharing our beliefs, here's what I believe," I continued. "I believe your hurt for losing Andrik has replaced that love for him you speak about. I don't believe there is any love in you right now." She began to cry. "And I believe, Jill—no, I *know* this. You have got to move from hurt to healing. There is no traction, no direction in hurt, it's a nasty trap." She pulled away, and stood, tears now streaming down her face, and pushing Arjun away as he tried to get close.

She walked a few steps toward her car, then turned, "Anything else you bitch?"

I took a deep breath, then walked to her, "As a matter of fact yes. Healing, Jill, healing is where you will create the direction, the will to move on." I paused, glancing to Arjun, then back to her, "and in that healing, love will return."

Our eyes locked for a moment, then she went to her car and pulled slowly from the lot.

I'll Never Feel Whole Again

Arjun cleaned the table in silence, dropping the bags into a nearby trashcan. I went to sit on a swing, focused on breathing slowly after my exchange with Jill. I rocked slightly, lost in my thoughts until I heard Arjun's engine fire up. It idled for a minute, then surprised me when I heard it turn off, and his door open and close. I stayed swinging, my eyes closed and face to the sun.

"Can I sit with you?" he asked, his eyes moist with tears. I smiled, nodding to the swing next to me. "Thank you."

"For what? I'm sitting here not sure I didn't make things worse by pissing off Jill more about you and me meeting."

"No Sammy. She was different this time. I saw something in her eyes when you talked about moving from hurt to healing." He paused, "I know she does not look it, or present herself this way now. Jill is a brilliant lady, with a huge heart and passion for being alive. She was a sought-after Sales executive in the banking world for years, and she was so wonderful at being that strong executive, and a beautiful wife and mother. For just an instant this morning, I saw a glimpse of that something in her eyes; that thing I haven't seen since Andrik's passing."

Arjun held out his hand and I took it as we rocked in unison. He asked about my thoughts on moving from hurt to healing, and I explained to him about the word "transhition," and the power of taking "h" out of the storm. I explained that people need to identify the negative force present in our struggle that begins with an "h", become conscious of it, work to remove it, and replace it with a positive force.

"Sounds to me like for Jill, for us, it's moving from hurting to healing." I nodded in agreement.

We walked to his car and Arjun slid behind the wheel then looked up to me, his hand on the ignition, "I am going to talk to Jill. We must keep talking with her. YOU must keep talking to her. I'm going to ask again that she and I meet with you."

I held my hand over my eyes, blocking the sun. "Do you think she will?"

Arjun smiled softly, "I do. Something happened over there, something small . . . and good. Yes, she'll agree to meet." He looked intently to me, nodding slowly, "Sammy, Jill was also adopted." He fired up the engine and pulled away.

I was sensing Jill was at—or near—her proverbial *rock bottom*, a hell of a place, full of despair, guilt, anger, hopelessness, and numbness. I remember back in my life the numbness I felt during my struggles, in my own transhitions. I now know that while rock bottom is this painful place, often a person must get there; without doing so, they cannot move forward, they cannot heal. I replayed my conversation with Jill, not sure I made a good enough distinction between hurting and healing, and made a mental note to revisit that with her if given the chance. I also added to that note to finish the definition of okay I had begun with Arjun, before he interrupted me to talk of Andrik and his obsessive car washing after his son died.

Late that evening, I decided to stroll along the beach by my hotel. Just as I was setting out, I heard the ping from my phone and found one new message. It was from Arjun.

> Arjun: Jill stayed in our bedroom most of the day, then came down to me in my office about 4. She asked if I would sit with her by the pool. We did, and for the first hour she said nothing. And then we talked. Sammy, it was so good. There was still anger and some yelling, and at one point, Jill said she felt something when you took her hand and wouldn't let go.

She said you reminded her of a very old nun (sorry, ha ha), Sister Patricia, that used to sit with her in the orphanage and hold her hand when she was angry. She said she feels she had a breakthrough

Me: This is so wonderful to hear. I'm happy for her, and for you.

Arjun: She wants to meet. At the house, just you two. She said I could join after. Can we do tomorrow morning at 10? I don't want to wait?

Me: sure, see you there.

The next morning, I was raising my hand to knock on Arjun and Jill's door when it opened. Arjun greeting me with a hug and led me to the kitchen where I took a cup of his cousin's tea, shaanti—I figured we would need all the peace we could get. He then motioned me to move to some poolside chairs.

"She seems okay this morning, not quite as good as last night, although she actually got a shower this morning. I heard it from the guest room, where I stay." He sighed. "We've not slept together since . . ." Arjun stopped talking at the sound of the French doors opening. Jill appeared, walking our way, her face very relaxed and neutral. She wore sandals and jeans, revealing thin legs usually hidden beneath baggy sweatpants. Her hair hung straight and damp, the wet ends making dark spots on the same gray soccer hoodie she wore each time I saw her.

"Good morning, Jill."

Hi."

Arjun rose to help her settle into a chair. "Would you like some tea, honey?"

She smiled slightly. "No, thanks. Please leave me alone with Sammy." Arjun placed his hand on her shoulder as he walked by on his way to the house. Jill took a few breaths, her eyes avoiding mine as she fidgeted to get comfortable in the chair, finally crossing her legs and arms. "First of all, I am sorry for calling you a bitch yesterday. It was hurtful."

I smiled, raising my teacup. "All good. Trust me, I've been called worse."

"Yeah, me too." She said, a slight grin appearing, causing small dimples I'd not seen before. "I didn't sleep too well last night. Actually, I don't really sleep well at all, unless I take a few pills, which I usually do more in the day." She shook her head. "You've never been a nun, have you?"

I laughed, "No, not even close. I definitely believe in the man—or woman—upstairs, and that we are here as an extension of our higher power, or God." I folded my hands in prayer, "I actually was in your world, so to speak, when I ran a venture capital firm on Wall Street."

She spread her fingers in front of her, then ran them through her hair. "No shit, really? I had you pegged for one of those life coach, personal growth, self-help people."

"I guess you could call me that now, I kind of had an epiphany one morning in a coffee shop with my friend Rachel. I'd had an all-nighter in Manhattan, drinking way too much champagne and tequila, and when the limo dropped me off at home as the sun was doing its thing, I just felt so empty . . . so lost." I paused, reflecting on my words. "Seems like a whole other life."

"What's your last name? My father worked on Wall Street for his entire career."

"Windermere."

She looked at the pool, biting her upper lip. "Sounds familiar. I remember him talking about a 'Sammy' that he worked with, and I was little, so I thought it was funny that a lady had a man's name."

"Yep, tell me about it."

"But that was a long time ago, and I'm guessing that lady would be a lot older than you, or maybe even dead at this point." A few birds pecked at the grass, working hard for some breakfast.

"Did Arjun tell you about the nun?" she continued. I nodded. "She was a special woman." Jill took a deep breath. "So many years ago, and yet I remember her well, and more the way she made me feel. Arjun told me he mentioned to you that I'd been adopted. I never knew my parents and never even looked for them. I guess its just one of those things. I went to live with a family for a few years, and then ended back up at the orphanage until my mom and dad adopted me.

"Just like you said a minute ago, I was so empty and lost. I used to sit on Sister Patricia's lap in the chapel, and she'd sing to me, and hold my hands." Tears filled her eyes as she stood and walked to the diving board, taking a seat on the edge. I waited, then followed, taking a seat next to her, and placing my arm around her. "She made me feel so good . . . so loved. There was something I felt when I held her hand; something that let me know it was all going to be okay."

She turned to me, her face full of the wetness of tears and a running nose. I pulled my arm down into my sleeve and wiped her face gently. "I felt that yesterday when you squeezed my hand, not letting go," Jill said. "Sammy, I cannot stay this empty and lost, I loved Andrik more than I ever thought I could love, and now its . . ." Her voice trailed off. After a minute, she continued. "At first I was not sure about his name, Andrik." She looked to me smiling gently, "I mean I was pushing for Michael, Patrick or Brendan. I'll tell you what though, when he was placed in my arms, with his dark hair and piercing dark eyes, he was my son, Andrik."

"It's a beautiful name, for a beautiful young man."

"Yes, he was. Sammy, can you make me lose this emptiness and despair?"

I took her hands, pulling her to her feet, and standing very close, our eyes locked. "No." Jill winced, her face full of questioning. "But *you* can. You are the one who needs to replace these feelings, this way of being with something better. I will support you in doing this as best I can; just know that you have to do the work, you have to walk your path of resilience." I paused, shaking her hands a few times, "If this is truly what you want."

"It is." She uttered softly, the tears coming again.

"OK, let me go get Arjun. We need him also."

The three of us settled at the table by the pool, a small cactus and some other potted plants standing guard around us. Arjun sat close to Jill, taking her hand in his.

"I talked with you yesterday about the difference between hurting and healing," they nodded in unison, "and I'm not quite sure I was clear. Hurt, the physical and emotional pain we feel in life, the heartache you both have, is normal. It's part of being human, and it invades many situations in life and takes over. Healing, on the other hand, is getting free of the hurt, getting back to being whole again. What I meant yesterday, and what we need to work on is this, it's the key to moving on. Please hear this loud and clear: it's not ever, ever about forgetting Andrik, it's about becoming whole again . . . " I paused, being sure to muster gentleness for my words, "It's about becoming whole again . . . without Andrik here."

"Does the hurt go away?" asked Arjun, placing his other hand atop Jill's.

I shook my head, "No. It just takes a back seat to healing. Your focus shifts to healing, and this is what begins driving you, not hurt, it's just along for the ride. It's part of the journey. You see, Jill and Arjun, we get what we focus on in life." I looked intently, glancing slowly back and forth at them. "You get what you focus on in life."

Jill smiled, letting out a small laugh, as Arjun and I turned to her. "I remember saying that same thing to Andrik before one of his championship soccer games in high school." Arjun looked at me, his bright smile sitting beneath his moist eyes.

"Yes," I continued, sure to maintain the positive energy I was feeling from Jill. "Focus, they say, is the concentration of attention or energy on something, it's what drives our action. So, you see, there will be a helluva difference in what you do, when you're focused on healing instead of hurting; and this difference in actions will help you recover. You welcome the hurt when it comes, and it will, you just understand that you can again become whole, the hurt and loss is just part of this transition." I ran my hands through my hair, then pursed my lips for a few seconds before finishing my thoughts, "it's like this. There's a subtle difference in thinking between hurt versus healing; and I ask you to trust me on this . . . it's one of those things in your life where it's better experienced than explained."

Jill spoke first after some silence. "I think I understand, and I can see we have to move to experience it, but—" she paused, and I waited to see what you would come after the word "but," trusting it wouldn't be an excuse as to why she couldn't do it. "Why does life have to be so shitty sometimes?"

Arjun looked to me, "Can I offer an answer?" I nodded, as Arjun pulled a small wallet from his back pocket, flipping it open to reveal a small paper pad, and pulling out a small pen. He wrote the word transition, leaving a blank in the middle, and then proceeded to do a wonderful job walking Jill through the simple teaching of taking the h out of transhition, glancing to me a few times as I offered an encouraging smile.

After he finished, Jill tore off the page from Arjun's notepad and turned to me, "I think I got it. My 'h' is hurt, and I can replace it with another word, healing. When I shift from just hurting, and allow my hurt, and my other emotions be a part of healing, then, then . . . " Jill did not finish and she did not need to; her tears and soft smile said it all. She was ready.

"So what do we do now? Where do we go from here?" Arjun asked rapidly, wanting to build some momentum from his teaching point.

"Well, remember I said it's about action. Close your eyes and think about what we discussed here, and Arjun's wonderful teaching." His cheeks reddened slightly, "Focus on healing; and only open them when you have brought to mind two actions you can take from the perspective of someone who is healing." I watched Arjun let go of Jill's hand, folding his and placing them in his lap. Jill's eyes closed slowly as she sat straight and took in a very deep breath.

Her eyes popped open only seconds after. "Got mine." Arjun opened his eyes, seeming surprised at the quickness with which Jill completed the exercise.

"OK, great. Arjun?"

"Yes, I have them also. Let Jill go." He turned to her, "What are your two, honey?"

She slid her chair back, resting her butt on the edge, her hands rubbing her jeans, the number 11 on the sleeve of her hoodie in full view. "First, go to visit Andrik." Arjun looked to me with concern. Jill had seen his look, and said to him. "I know, I know." She looked back to me, "Sammy, I have not been to the cemetery since his funeral." Then she took Arjun's hand, "And this, is something a mother would do who is healing."

Arjun spoke, "This is mine as well, I was just scared to say it."

"Yes, it's okay Arjun. Fear walks with us on the path of healing; perhaps work to see it as our friend. Where there is fear of doing something, there is healing on the other side." He nodded.

"And your second?" I asked Jill.

A smile crossed her face, "Go to a soccer game at the field where Andrik used to play."

Arjun smiled fiddling with his fingers. I looked to him, "And your second."

He went behind Jill, wrapping his arms around her waist. "This is good for now. We have two good ones."

Arjun cleared the teacups, taking them to the kitchen. Jill and I sat still, taking in the soothing sounds of the water spilling off some rocks and into the hot tub at the end of the pool. Birds chirped as the clouds drifted about the sky, sending occasional shadows down. Arjun returned, taking his seat and breaking the silence of nature. "When should we go? To the cemetery I mean?" He and I looked to Jill, whose stare was fixed on the surface of the pool.

She stood, "Now." She said in a strong voice, turning to walk toward the house. "Just give me a few minutes. Andrik does not need to see me wearing his old soccer hoodie." Arjun excused himself. I remained on the patio, walking slowly around the pool, stopping once to slip my sandal off and skim my foot across the surface of the water. I was thinking about Jill, and our pending visit to Andrik's grave, not sure if she would be okay, or have a setback on her journey of healing.

Accepting Reality

"Happiness can exist only in acceptance."
- George Orwell

About 10 minutes later, Arjun came through the kitchen door, followed by Jill, a woman I almost did not recognize. Her hair was dry now, with soft curls falling on her shoulders. She wore white jeans, sandals and a deep green blouse that accented her pale, smooth skin and auburn hair, appearing lighter than when it was pulled back by a headband.

"Ready?" she asked. She walked more confidently and stood taller.

"Not yet." I responded, let's sit for just a minute, I have something I need to say to Arjun that was interrupted yesterday. "It will be good for both of you to hear it." They wore blended looks of concern and curiosity as they sat with me at the table, and I turned to Arjun.

"You asked me yesterday in the park 'Why do you keep saying it's all gonna be okay?', and I began to offer you the definition of 'okay.' This is vital for both of you to understand as you move through this tragic time. The definition of 'okay' is to express, or be in a state of agreement or acceptance." I paused, the three of us looking at one another like poker players. "Agreement or acceptance. A person is okay when one of these is present, regardless of what's happening in their life, and it's not always the proverbial smooth sailing, sometimes it's just flat out brutally painful. I get that you don't 'agree' with what happened to Andrik and losing him, who would? Right?" Jill nodded as she reached for Arjun's hand. "And please, please, please hear me on this . . . what is possible here is that you get to *acceptance*, and you move away from being broken and beaten down."

Their eyes were squinting, and mouths closed, concentrating on what I'd said. Jill stood, "Let's go."

"And you look great." I spoke.

"Thank you." Jill nodded with a smile, taking Arjun's hand, as the three of us set off down the brick walkway.

The 15-minute ride to the cemetery was filled with a few minutes of small talk, and mostly silence. Jill shifted in the front passenger seat as the car slowed, turning right through the gates of the cemetery. Arjun pulled the car to the side of the entrance, a road lined with manicured lawns and flower beds that could have been mistaken for the entrance into Augusta National Golf Club; the only likely difference being the perfectly spaced palm trees lining the road like sentinels standing guard. Jill's breathing quickened.

Arjun put the car in park and came around to open Jill's door. He squatted down, his eyes fixed on her, with only a quick glance past the headrest to me. "We don't have to do this." She stayed still, staring straight through the windshield. "If you're not ready, we can go home and come back another time."

He glanced to me, and I nodded slightly as Jill turned to him. "No, no, let's keep going." Arjun kissed her head, got back in the SUV, and began driving. A few turns led us to the edge of the cemetery, where a collection of headstones sat nestled against a small, sparkling lake. Arjun turned off the engine, and he and I got out of the car. We stood next to the passenger door until Jill opened it, standing slowly, and taking even slower breaths. A few men dressed in overalls rode by on a small farm like vehicle, smiled politely and continued, shovels and other tools laying across the back bed. Jill grabbed Arjun's arm with both hands, as I followed them onto the grass and to a medium sized headstone at the edge of the lake under a palm tree. I slowed my pace, allowing them to arrive at the stone, standing together, arm in arm. I remained behind them. Neither said a word, their heads bowed, staring at the stone.

Jill let out a chilling sob, collapsing to her knees, her hands hanging onto the stone, as Arjun knelt beside her. The men in overalls had stopped at a pile of dirt a few rows over and turned quickly, one bowed his head, then returned to digging. I thought of how many times they'd witnessed this scene, and wondered if they'd become numb to it, or did it plant seeds of inspiration for them to go home after work and say, "I love you." Her sobs continued, slowing, and softening after a few minutes. She stood and began to walk along the lake, Arjun began to follow until Jill turned, shaking her head, and putting her palm up at him. She held a tissue to her eyes, her face twisted in anguish.

I moved graveside, noticing the years of Andrik's birth and death, separated by a dash, and adding up to just over 20 years of life here on Earth. A warmth filled me as I saw the number 11, engraved in the stone between quotations mark, in the middle of his first and last name. Arjun came to stand with me, I placed my hand in his, turning slightly, "Let her be." He nodded, wiping his nose as a tear slid down his cheek.

A few minutes passed, just the sound of birds, the wind and shovels moving dirt were heard. "Eleven was Andrik's number. Jill used to call him that. 'How you doing there, Eleven? All set for the game?' she would joke with him when he came down for breakfast before high school. Then she would always text a similar message once he went off to the university. It was good it was not far, and we were able to make most of the games."

We turned a few minutes later, hearing Jill sniffling and walking our way. Her white jeans were stained at the knees, and she held an overused tissue. She came to us, wrapping us in her hug without saying a word. When we parted, she smiled a bit, knelt again, and sat back on her feet, laying her hand on the bottom of the stone. "Hi, honey. It's

Mom and Dad, and our friend Sammy. I know I haven't been here in a long time, and I'm sorry."

She began to cry, her words coming out slurred. "I've not been a good mom that way. I should have come more. It's just," she took a few deep breaths, "It's just that I was having a really hard time without you. Now, though, honey, now, I am moving to accept your leaving us way too soon. I see that acceptance is what I must do or your dad will not have only lost you, he will have lost me too." She stood. "So, Eleven, please know how much I did—and still do—love you and miss you. I'll be back, I promise." She pulled her phone from her back pocket, took a picture of the stone, then tapped the screen a few times before sliding it back into her jeans.

We walked to the car in silence, a few feet apart from one another, lost in our thoughts. Jill arrived first, leaning against the front hood, and pulling her phone out. She hit the screen and held it to us, showing the picture of Andrik's tombstone, his smiling face looking at us from the picture embossed into the stone. It was her screensaver now, and she smiled gently. "I'm gonna be okay."

Hurt Has No Ticket to This Game

Arjun called the next morning and told me he and Jill had a nice evening after our visit to see Andrik. He said he heard Jill get up very early this morning and go downstairs, then heard a splash. He hurried to the window of his room and saw Jill in the pool. It was the first time she'd done an early morning swim since Andrik's death. But now he was concerned as she'd been swimming for hours, every now and again sitting on the side of the pool for a few minutes, staring at the water, then getting back to it. "What should I do?" he asked. I suggested he make some tea and watch her from the window, and call me when she stops.

Thirty minutes later, Arjun called. "I went out to sit by the pool, watching Jill. Again, she stopped and sat on the edge of the pool, but this time noticed me. She smiled sadly, then began to cry. I went and sat with her, saying nothing, just with my arm around her and our feet in the pool. She told me about a dream she had. She was sitting at Andrik's grave, and he came and sat next to her."

"Did Andrik say anything in the dream?" Arjun was quiet. "Arjun?"

"I am here. Yes, Andrik told Jill he did not want her to come visit him anymore. He said she only came because 'that lady' made her. He said he didn't want her to do anything she didn't want to do."

"I understand. And how is she now? Did she stop swimming?"

"Yes, she did, probably after going a few miles. She said she was going to shower and lie down."

"Okay, are you going to be there all day?"

"Yes, I'm not leaving. I'm worried about this, about her." He whispered.

"Do me a favor and ask her if I can come over." He began to interrupt, saying maybe it was not a good idea. "Arjun, listen to me. I understand she's upset, but I need to talk with her today." I paused, wanting to make sure he did what I asked. "Arjun, this is very normal. I know that sounds crazy, and I'll explain. I must talk with her."

Later that day, the three of us were sitting at the kitchen table. There was no tea, or snacks or anything, just the three of us. Jill's sad eyes looked from Arjun to me, her hands folded on the table. She was wearing a plain black t-shirt and matching yoga pants.

"Jill, thanks for letting me visit. I can guess that when you woke from your dream you never wanted to see me again," I said. She nodded, tears in her eyes, tissue in hand. "Here's something I want you to consider—We . . . you . . . are designed with a brain whose main job is to keep you safe, to protect you from harm." I reached out, placing my hand on Jill's. "From hurt."

Arjun chimed in, "But why the dream?"

"I believe the dream was your brain doing its work, using your powerful subconscious mind to get you to not go visit Andrik, to not take the actions of someone on a path of healing, because of the hurt."

Jill finally spoke. "But hurt is the 'h' word we said we need to take out of this transhit . . . this transition,."

"It is. And we are," I said with intensity, my voice firm with conviction. "When we focus on healing, and take actions from that place, there is still hurt. It has to be here, it's a key part of the healing journey. Just remember, please remember this . . . you cannot let the hurt be in charge or you will spend your life in this intense pain you're experiencing."

"So, my brain is working to get me to not take actions that are a threat to me; things that will upset me?" she asked.

"Yes, it would rather have you hanging out here at the house in the cloud of numbness. And think about what we discussed regarding acceptance; the sense of being okay. The more you visit Andrik's grave, the hurt will subside, your acceptance will grow, and you become okay with your life."

Jill asked silently, staring at her folded hands on the table. "Will the hurt go away?"

I slid my chair next to her, taking both hands and staring into her eyes. "No, never entirely. What will happen, is the abundance of hurt you have for losing Andrik, for not having him now, will be replaced with love." I spoke with emphasis. "The love of having had him in your life for those 20 years."

"And that . . . that is healing." Arjun whispered slowly. He stood and placed his hands on Jill's shoulders.

She smiled, laughing nervously as tears flowed. "And that is healing." She stammered.

* * *

Two weeks passed, and I stayed in touch with the grieving parents. Jill had even given me her phone number and we'd texted one another occasionally. She was swimming almost every morning, had visited Andrik's grave a few more times, and reported there were no more dreams. I was in the middle of dropping in on another client of mine, a beautiful man nearing the end of his short life, when my phone buzzed.

> Jill: Hi. Arjun and I are going to a soccer game tomorrow morning. Andrik's club team is playing. Can you make it?
>
> Me: Absolutely. See you there

Jill: Thanks. 10:00. The field is in the park where you met Arjun . . . and I called you that flattering name that rhymes with witch. Sorry again 😉

Me: All good. Have a nice night. See you in the morning.

The next morning, I pulled into the lot; parking next to Arjun's top-down Porsche. Jumping from my Jeep I noticed two suitcases in the back seat of the Porsche. My mind raced for an explanation, until it was called back when I heard Arjun yell my name. He stood in the metal bleachers, facing me, and waving with one hand and holding up a cup of coffee in the other.

"Well, good morning, you two," I said after snaking my way up a few rows through a bunch of soccer fans. Jill wore a t-shirt sporting the soccer team's logo, and Arjun a matching baseball hat. I smiled, hugged Jill, and gave Arjun a fist bump as he handed me a cup of steaming coffee. "Perfect. Thanks."

The teams were introduced, and we stood for the National Anthem. Arjun took Jill's hand as she wiped tears away. A few people stopped to say hello during the game and intermissions, some mentioning Andrik and offering hugs. Andrik's club scored the winning goal with less than a minute left. His friend and former teammate, Vic, got a breakaway, made a phenomenal move where he rolled the ball out on his right foot as the goalie charged toward him, then pulled it back, flicking the ball behind his left leg, which left the goalie stumbling as Vic's left foot rolled the ball into the net. As Vic ran by the sideline, being hugged by teammates, he looked to Jill and Arjun, offering a smile, and holding up a peace sign. We were on our feet cheering, and I'm pretty sure the tears rolling down Jill's cheeks were those of joy and healing. Hurt did not have a ticket to this game.

We mingled in a sea of the team colors of navy and white with the players, parents, and coaches for a few minutes, then walked to our cars.

Jill took a seat on my front bumper, patting the place next to her as an invitation for me to join. I did, as Arjun reached into the front seat of his car, pulled out a small, wrapped box, and handed it to Jill. She took the box, holding it gently in her hands, her fingers fiddling with the bright yellow bow. She handed it to me. "What's this?" I asked, tilting my head.

"Something Arjun and I want you to have," she said, placing a hand on my shoulder.

I opened the small box and lifted out a small silver pendant of the sun hanging on a smooth leather cord. "It's beautiful."

"Andrik gave it to me on my 50th birthday."

"Oh, Jill, I cannot take this. I—"

Jill interrupted, sitting straight, and pointing her finger at me. "Sammy, you can, and you will." She looked playfully to Arjun. "Don't make me get nasty with you again." I laughed, shaking my head from side to side.

"Andrik said it would always remind me of him when I wore it, you know, because of his name meaning the sun rising between the mountains." Jill began to cry, fighting to get the words out. "Sammy, because of you, I don't need this anymore. I don't need to be reminded of him." She pulled the arm of her t-shirt, wiped tears from her eyes, and let out a nervous laugh. "He's here, he's with me, he's with us. I know this now." She stood, took the necklace from me, and put it around my neck. I looked at this small sun hanging on my chest. I felt good, I felt warmth.

We all hugged, me holding them each by an arm when we parted. "Just one question," I said, pursing my lips and pulling them to the side. "The suitcases?"

"Oh, those," Arjun smirked, "that's my second action to take from a place of healing. You remember I only told you one."

"Go on." I said.

"We're leaving right now for two weeks in the Keys, a small cottage at the end of a quiet street, with a path leading through the dense vegetation to a peaceful beach. We're gonna swim, smile, and update a resume.'" He looked to Jill, who smiled as he took her in his arms. "And most of all, we're going to watch the sun greet us each morning and say goodbye to it each night."

"Perfect." I stood, watching the Porsche back out of the spot, inspired by the two wonderful people in sunglasses, smiling and waving to me. I took the sun hanging from my neck in my fingers, caressing it gently, tears coming as I read the letters on the license plate: ELEVEN.

— 5 —

Natalie

"No man is crushed by misfortune unless he has first been deceived by prosperity."

– Seneca

Natalie Alone

I breathed in the fresh, salty aroma of the Pacific Ocean as I wheeled my Porsche north through Malibu. Every time I drove this part of the PCH—Pacific Coast Highway—I would look up at Pepperdine University, sitting high on the hill atop the massive emerald lawn, and wonder if the students really appreciated the view as they walked to their classes. My boss had contacted me about a woman who may need, hmmmm, what did she call it? Yes, "some observations for consideration," is what she said, knowing full well I interpreted that phrase to mean *this was gonna be a tough one.*

I pulled into the cobblestone-covered entrance of the luxury hotel in Montecito; the bright white facade, red terracotta-tiled roof, and expensive vehicles supported its reputation as the place to stay in the Santa Barbara area. The valet attendant, a Hispanic man with a bright smile, full head of gray hair, and eyes that sparkled like the blue ocean I'd been watching over the past hour, smiled as he opened my door. "Hello ma'am, welcome to the Inn. I love your car, a classic for sure." He opened the door for me. "You look just like an angel floating in on a cloud." His warmth and natural need to serve others was obvious.

I smiled and handed him a $20 bill. "Thanks, I bet you say that to all the women in white convertibles."

He laughed, nodding. "Thank you. No ma'am, I confess this is the first time I used that line in my 40 years here at the Inn, not sure where it even came from. Will you be staying with us, ma'am?" He tore a ticket in two and handed me half.

"Yes, for a day or two. And please, call me Sammy."

I gave him a thumbs-up and walked to the front desk. My ankle length skirt waved in the soft breeze, and my sandals clicked on the gleaming tile floor. I asked the young lady at the front desk to call the person I was to meet. "Oh, you must be Miss Windermere?" I nodded. "Miss Mitchell told me to have you walk down the street to meet her at a restaurant just down the street called Lucky's. She'll be in the bar."

I thanked her and headed to the door. *OK.* I thought. *This makes sense based on what I know about this woman.*

I walked slowly as Lucky's was less than a football field away. The street was bustling; people ducked in and out of the shops filled with ridiculously overpriced goods. Maserati's, Lamborghini's, and Range Rovers were scattered among the parking spots.

I entered Lucky's, smiling at the woman at the hostess stand. "Hi. I 'm meeting someone in the bar." A muscular man sitting on a bench in the corner looked up from his paper and caught my eye. There was a sliver of a smile on his face. He glanced into the bar, then resumed reading.

"Yes." The hostess nodded. "Ms. Mitchell is expecting you." She pointed to the far end of the bar.

Natalie Mitchell had a martini glass in front of her. She was tapping and swiping across the surface of her phone. She glanced to me, nodded, then returned to her swiping. She looked up as I stopped next to her.

So, this is the great Natalie Mitchell, the entrepreneur who's been a guest on countless talk shows and news segments and whose image has been on countless magazine covers.

"Yes?" she said, as she removed her glasses.

"Hello, Natalie, I'm Sammy Windermere." I extended my hand. She looked at it, then back to me with a hit of surprise, and slowly extended hers.

"Forgive me if I look surprised. I was expecting someone younger." She sipped her drink, two olives stuck with a stick lay at the bottom. "Oh, no offense intended."

"None taken. May I?" I asked, sliding onto the barstool before she could answer.

"Of course." She said, glancing to her phone one more time before laying it down on the bar between us. "Robert," she called to the bartender in a directive tone, "please get Ms. Windermere here a drink." I ordered a glass of Sauvignon Blanc.

"So here we are." She said, stirring her half-done drink with the stick. She turned to me, tilting her head sideways. "That's obvious, right? The question I have is—" she paused—"why are we here?" Her hair was short and gray, styled in a way that made her look younger than her seventy-plus years. Her black yoga pants, white sneakers, white designer top, and Apple watch suggested a woman quite a few years from retirement. Retirement was not a word I guessed was in her vocabulary, as she could have done that a long time ago. No, this woman did not need retirement.

"You beat me to it, Ms. Mitchell. That is the question I have for you."

"Well, it seems—" she took a deep breath, her bright teeth showing against her smooth, ebony skin. She continued, "It seems we're here because my ex-husband, John, is worried about me, and he got in touch with someone who knows you and suggested we meet. I don't normally jump when my ex-husband says to, but he called in a favor, so here I am."

She sipped her drink. "Ms. Windermere. We don't know one another, and I was surprised when my staff did some research and could not find you."

"Yes, I keep a low profile, so to speak. My work, my meeting with people like you, comes from my boss, who has a tremendous network." I smiled after taking a sip of my slightly chilled wine. "What would you like to know? And you can call me Sammy."

"Ms. Windermere," she said smugly, "as you likely know, I'm a very busy woman. The only reason I'm here is to appease John. I'd just simply like an answer to my question, 'Why are we here?'"

"It seems we're here—and again, the answer is ultimately yours—because John loves you and is concerned about you and what you're dealing with right now. He thought it might help you to have someone, um, neutral to talk to. He thinks the stress may be affecting your health."

Robert walked by slowly, placing a small bowl of nuts between us. Natalie waved him away. "Look, John is a good man. I still love him, but I'm happy that he remarried and has a few kids and grandkids, and a wife who makes him feel appreciated." She looked to me intently, her brown eyes not blinking. "That's why he left you know, he said he was not appreciated. I was very busy then building Ollopa; I didn't have time to appreciate him, or anyone for that matter. I took care of a lot of people, John at the top of the list. Well, let me tell you, he got a hell of a lot of money from me for not feeling," she rolled her eyes and held up her fingers in quotation marks, "appreciated." Her fingers fiddled with the napkin beneath her glass. "Do I miss being married to him? Absolutely not."

"I understand."

"Are you married?"

"No."

"Ever been?"

"No, like you I focused on my career."

"Career?"

"Yes. Wall Street. Hedge Funds."

Natalie pursed her lips together, placing her index finger below her nose. It was her classic pose, often used on many of the covers. "Well, perhaps you will tell me more about that sometime."

"I'd be happy to, but I'd rather talk about you."

She took a sip of her drink, leaving a small amount in the bottom of the glass. She picked the up the olive-laden wooden stick and waved it slowly. She looked down as her phone buzzed, then to me. "I need to go take care of something, so let me do my best to be clear. What I'm going through doesn't scare me one bit, nor is it impacting my health, despite whatever John told your boss. This little bitch who thinks she won . . ." She paused, placing the stick between her gleaming teeth, and pulling off one olive. "Well, Ms. Windermere, she has not. This game is far from over. She'll be sorry, trust me." I nodded as Natalie stood, her face full of intensity, and directed Robert to put this on her tab. "I'll meet you the three times John told me was the agreement, and this counts as one. Please, though, please, don't tell me what I need to do."

I stood and offered my hand. She took it and I held on as she began to pull away, our eyes locked. "Ms. Mitchell, my job never is to tell people what to do. That doesn't bring about learning or growth. What I may do is offer you a few observations for your consideration." She pulled her hand slowly from mine. "That's all."

Natalie walked a few steps toward the door, before turning back. "I have lunch with 'O' and her people tomorrow at noon. They may do a feature on me in her magazine. Meet me in the hotel lobby at six a.m. We'll take a sunrise hike. And that will be meeting number two." She turned and walked away, assuming I would be impressed she is friends with the iconic talk-show host and one-woman brand. I watched her leave the bar, and the saw the muscular man follow her out.

I sat back down, taking a small sip of the refreshing wine. *Wow, she is all she's made out to be. Okay, meeting number two in the morning.* I pulled some bills from my pocket as Robert was clearing the bar.

"Oh, no ma'am, this is on Ms. Mitchell."

"Thank you, Robert. She a good tipper?"

He smiled, raising his eyebrows, and wearing a warm smirk, "Sometimes yes, sometimes no. She's a piece of work for sure."

I winked, dropped a $20 bill on the bar and headed out.

Everybody's Against Me

I entered the cool, darkened, lobby before six o'clock, intent on enjoying some coffee before my hike with Natalie. As I walked to the coffee stand, I noticed the muscular man sitting on a sofa, dressed in black hiking shorts and a zip up jacket. Again, he smiled slightly, seemingly saying, *Yes, you'll be seeing a lot of me.* I returned his smile, poured some steaming coffee, and took a seat near the front door. The elevator doors opened a few minutes later and Natalie walked to the coffee stand confidently. She poured a cup, glancing to the muscular man, and nodded. He was up and out of the lobby quickly. Natalie turned, took a sip and peered over the rim of the mug, her eyes catching mine.

"Early. Good. I like that," she said as she took the seat next to me.

"Good morning, Natalie. Yes, my dad always told me 'to be early is to be on time.'"

"I like your Dad."

"Oh, yes, I'm sure he would have liked you too."

"So, meeting number two. You ready?" she said.

"Sure. You?"

"Do I have a choice? I mean, I pondered the thought of canceling this morning, although John's nagging voice in my head told me otherwise."

"You always have a choice. I'm fine either way," I said. I took the last sip of my coffee then dropped my cup in a nearby trash can. I turned back to see Natalie walking out the door. I scurried to catch up with her, and we set off down the street, turning left at the light and beginning our way uphill toward the mountains.

"Trey will be with us," she said, giving her head a slight flip. I turned to see him behind us, walking tall and strong in his black gear. Natalie turned to me. "There are a few people that would probably be very happy if I had a hiking accident this morning."

We walked briskly through town then made our way behind what looked like another hotel. Not far down the back drive we stopped at a trailhead where the sign read McGovern Trail.

"You okay?" Natalie asked, pulling her water bottle from its pocket on her belt and taking a sip as perspiration shined on her face. "Pace good for you?"

"Good warm-up. You ready to talk?" I put my bottle back in the holder, and saw Trey not far behind, his eyes hidden behind his sunglasses and no doubt always scanning our surroundings.

"Not yet. The next part is steep, so let's wait to talk until we reach the top." Natalie stood tall, took in a deep breath, and headed up the dirt trail, mumbling something about warm-up.

We hiked over tree roots, rocks, and boulders, stopping only once for a water break. About a half hour later as we climbed around a corner, a bench sitting next to some huge boulders came into view. Natalie picked up her pace, finishing with a jog to the bench. I stayed with her.

Natalie sat on the edge of the bench; the blue expanse of the Pacific Ocean below reached to the horizon. The sun was rising to our left, replacing the morning chill with its warmth. Trey walked up to us slowly. "All good, Natalie?" She smiled as he took his place on a rock not far away.

I pulled the navy bandanna from my head and wiped the sweat from my face.

"So," Natalie said, letting it hang in the air for a moment. "What do you think about my situation? I'm sure you've heard about it. The headlines have labeled it a hostile takeover by a woman I mentored and groomed. The bitch is turning around to bite the hand that fed her."

"Yes. I have. Sounds very nasty from what the press is saying about it."

"That's one word for it." She put her legs straight in front of her, flexing her ankles. "The other word I like best is shitshow." She turned to me. "You know what that is, right?"

"I sure do. I've starred in many of them myself."

Natalie, stood, bending at the waist to stretch. "My early life was very easy; great family, good schools, nice friends." She gazed to the ocean. "Then once I got to college, the air of competition became very thick, and I loved it. It was like I found what was missing. I couldn't study hard or long enough, and I wanted the best internships and strongest network. I finished undergrad in less than four years and went right into Wharton, certain the education there would lay a foundation that would help me scale the heights even though I was a black woman in a white man's world."

She paused for a few minutes. "For many years, growing the business and leading people was fun, it seemed easier. I had plenty of challenges and problems, but I persevered. That's what I became famous for. I just keep going. And that's how I got through the hard times." She continued, reflecting, "I thought life would get easier at this stage of my life. I guess the world has changed, people have changed. I don't know if this situation is another shitshow in my life, or it's the continuation of the one I've been living for a long time."

"Do you enjoy them?"

"It seems all I know lately. And I'm not sure success is available without them."

I took a deep breath and stared at the sun's rays twinkling on the ocean.

"What? You think differently?"

I nodded slowly. "Yes. The shows—the situations we all deal with in life where there's pain, and struggle, sadness, despair, and risk, uncertainty, and fear—we're all gonna have them. The shit? That's a different story. We have some control over how much shit we allow in our lives because we can choose how we deal with the show, how we move through it, and whether we work on bringing a positive focus to what is certainly a negative situation." I turned to Natalie, her back straight and eyes wide.

"Let's get one thing straight here," she said. "I'm not afraid of anything or anyone. And those other feelings around right now—hurt, betrayal, anger? Well, I just push them back down when they show up."

"What if you didn't? What if you welcomed *all* the feelings and emotions you have about your mentee, your trusted friend and student? Her name's Diana, right? What if you just talked about all the different ways that Diana has messed up your life? What's she's doing to get your company from you? How do you feel about all this that's taking place?"

Natalie snapped, "That little . . ." She took a deep breath, glancing to Trey who became more fixed on us at the rise in Natalie's voice. "Diana is trying to steal my company, plain and simple. Hostile takeover? That's the politically correct description for theft, deceit, greed and evil. That's the stuff I need to deal with, and I will. She and the others she has recruited will NOT get Ollopa, even if this battle takes me to my grave."

"Okay, got it."

"Got what? I don't think you see! It's been my victories in the shitshows of my life that have gotten me to where I am today. It's why I have all the money, the success, the influence that I have." She paused. I rose from the bench and stood next to her.

"This stuff, talking about personal growth, self-help stuff, that's for other, unsuccessful people, it's not for me," she said. She looked to Trey, then turned to the trail. "No, I'm good. The more shit in my show, the better." She swept her hand toward the trail, suggesting I take the lead. "Let's head back. Do you want to go fast?"

I finished tying my bandanna. "Depends . . . the faster I go, the less I see."

I took off down the trail, stopping after a short distance. My feet moved quickly, even breaking into a jog at several points as we turned and slipped down the rocky trail.

We finished the hike in silence, retracing our path down through the mansions of Montecito. Natalie pointed out the road that "O's" house was on, saying she looked forward to lunch there later. As we walked into the lobby, Natalie fiddled with her watch, checking our mileage, our pace, and the elevated number she'd driven her heart rate to. "Always good to push it a bit. How did you feel?"

"Great hike, thanks for asking me to go along." I paused, handing her a glass of water from the large container along the wall. "You're in very good shape." Julio, the valet with the infectious smile, recognized me, and handed us some small towels to dry our perspiration.

"Have to be . . . when you feel like you're in a war every day." She scanned the lobby, running a hand through her hair. "Leave your number with the front desk. I have to leave in a day or two so I'll be sure to schedule our third meeting, then we can wish each other well and get back to our lives."

Can we sit for a minute first?" I asked. Natalie looked at her watch, then to Trey, who stood by the elevator.

"I really—"

I interrupted, my hand firmly on her arm. "Just for a few minutes."

She's Going to Pay

We moved to the floral covered chairs near one wall. "Tell me about Ollopa. Why did you work so hard to build it?"

Natalie smiled. My question seemed to take her back in time, and her shoulders dropped as she placed her cup on the side table, its condensation forming a small puddle on the glass top.

"Many years ago, my career in the financial world was going well. By chance, it seemed, I saw an opportunity to buy a small company from a man named Matthew. It was a good-sized medical device company in New Jersey, and I knew I could grow it, and diversify into other areas of healthcare, even into research to develop new ways to heal and improve the quality of life for so many," she said. "Matthew had started in his garage; he was a wonderful engineer with such an innovative and inquisitive mindset. Many people say they started their business to help people and they're full of shit. Matthew though, was different. He really meant it."

Natalie took another sip of water then continued. "He ran the company for over 30 years. After selling the company to me, he and his wife were going to spend the winters at their place in Florida and do some traveling, golfing, and most of all enjoying his beautiful family. He absolutely loved his young grandkids. The deal went well; he was such a fine businessman, and an even finer gentleman—so full of worthy values." She ran the towel across her face and wiped her eyes. "The sad thing is he died two months after the sale of his company; brain aneurysm. He didn't even get one full winter in Florida. He was only 68." Natalie's eyes narrowed, her lips pursed, and she shook her head. "He was a good man, a very good man . . . and friend. I wish he was here right now so I could talk with him."

"I'm sorry."

"Me too. I think of him often." She took a deep breath, and seemed to blow out the past memory of him. "After his death, I knew I had to grow the company, I had to use the company to help many more people. That's what Matthew would have wanted. I changed the name to Ollopa. I'm sure you know it's Apollo backwards." I nodded. "I always connected with Apollo when I learned about him in school. He could see into the future, had the power to heal, and was deadly with his bow-and-arrow in battle—all qualities I wanted to have. I had researched the female gods, too, but just felt connected to Apollo, to his strength." She paused, "Guess I should have been born a man."

Natalie nodded at Trey, and he walked over to the elevators.

I smiled softly.

"The best answer to your question is this . . . I wanted to build and lead a company whose mission was simply to heal, to end suffering." She stood.

"Is that still the reason you want to keep running Ollopa, the reason you want to prevent Diana from taking it over?"

Natalie looked at Trey, who was holding the elevator door open, then to me. Her face softened in its expression; her eyes grew gentler, maybe even showing a trace of vulnerability. "I'm not sure." She turned and entered the elevator.

I sat for what felt like a long time, staring through the open doors at the fountain in the courtyard. A stern voice snapped me from my trance, "Ms. Windermere." I turned to see Trey standing next to me. "Something has happened that Ms. Mitchell wants you to know about. Please follow me."

I stood, following this man who looked like an All-Pro football player to the elevator, then to Natalie's suite located on the top floor. Trey led me to a sitting room with bright white walls, and windows trimmed in dark brown wood with matching shutters. The windows offered wonderful views of the mountains on one side and the ocean on the other. A moment later Natalie came into the room, wearing a thick white robe bearing the Inn's logo on the chest; her face was filled with stress.

She took a seat on the cream sofa, placing her phone on the glass table, and motioning for me to join her. "I received a call from our pilot. My jet has been vandalized, and he said it was a professional job. A routine check caught it." She paused. "Had it not been found it likely would have caused a crash. It'll be grounded for a week."

I slid onto the sofa, watching as Natalie sank into a thoughtful silence. Then suddenly she picked up her phone. "I'm going to call Diana." She turned to the other room, "Trey, record this please." Trey entered, pulling a small, black device from his pocket, placing it on the table next to Natalie's phone.

Natalie touched the screen a few times, finally tapping the *speaker* icon, and the phone began to ring.

After the third ring, a woman's voice answered. "Natalie, what a nice surprise."

Natalie leaned toward the phone, her elbows resting on her thighs. "Oh, I'm sure you're all smiles."

"How can I help you?"

"Well, I'm here in California and just received a call from my pilot that my plane has been vandalized, perhaps I should say sabotaged." She paused and silence filled the room. "Had it not been discovered; the plane likely would have crashed."

Natalie's gaze stayed fixed on the phone, her lips closed, and eyes narrowed.

"Oh my God, Natalie! It's good it was discovered?"

"Is it?

"Natalie." Diana's voice was solid and stern. "I'm sure Trey is recording this, so hear me, and hear me well. I know nothing about this incident, nothing. You certainly know where I stand on the takeover, but I would never do anything to harm you or others. Even with what we're going through, I'm sad that the thought of me being involved in this even crossed your mind. I know you have enemies; I am not one. Natalie, you run around with Trey at your side like you're the President or Queen . . . But you know what?" Diana paused. "If you were ever kidnapped, I'm not sure there's anyone that would pay the ransom."

Natalie's face tightened; her fists clenched. "Oh, that's just great. You do know you'd be just another medical sales rep if it weren't for me." She let that comment settle in for Diana, who remained silent. "Then who Diana? Who in your camp would be ruthless enough?"

"Not one of them. My team and I have worked hard to put together a solid, reputable group."

"That's bullshit, Diana, and you know it." Natalie was on the verge of yelling. "You've got some people who are obsessed with taking my company away from me. They want all the profits that come with it."

"Natalie, I do not like you, who you've become. Do I hate you? No. In a way I feel sorry for you." She paused, "I would never do anything to harm you."

Natalie screamed, her face tight, and a large vein showing in her neck. "You're harming me now by trying to steal my company!"

An uncomfortable silence passed. Then Diana finally said, "You should hold up the mirror, Natalie. You're the one doing yourself harm. When I came to work at Ollopa, I was so thankful. I'd have worked for nothing, because the spirit of the company was amazing. I know you had this reputation for being a real brutal CEO, and dealmaker. But I saw your other side; how you treated those committed to your passion, your purpose to heal people; to improve the lives of those suffering. I believe many mistook your passion and gave it negative labels. And then, Natalie, then something happened to you. I'm not sure how, why, or when, something just happened. You became more focused on flying around to all your homes, and doing deals to "win," and the win was not about how the company could contribute to our purpose. It became about money, and celebrity, and revenge, and a whole bunch of other stuff."

Natalie sat staring at the phone.

Diana continued. "It makes me sad you think I'm leading this takeover because of the money. Take another look—really look—at who's on my side, and you'll see they're all committed to Ollopa's mission . . . to heal, to lessen suffering. You used to tell me the money was just a result of operating the business so we could deliver on our mission. I have a meeting to get to so just hear me on this, and I'll make it very clear. The reason this takeover is happening—and it will happen—is because me, and many others, don't believe that's how you think anymore." The line went dead.

Natalie stared at the phone, and then slowly left the room. I looked to Trey, who nodded for me to leave.

Later that night, after I had updated my boss about how things were going—or not—with Natalie, my phone buzzed. It was a text from her.

> Natalie: It's Natalie. I got a plane. Heading to Scottsdale at 7 in the morning. Meeting with my attorney to discuss my situation. Someone has to pay for this. If you come, we can call the trip meeting #3.
>
> Me: OK, I'll be there.
>
> Natalie: I feel like I'm just hanging on

Early the next morning the light of the sun was peaking over the mountains as I pulled my Porsche through the gate for private flights at the airport. A bearded man in the booth came out with a clipboard, checked my ID, and waved me through. A gleaming white Gulfstream sat next to a nearby hangar, a black Mercedes at the bottom of the steps. I put up the top of the Porsche, grabbed my bag from the front seat and smiled at my reflection in the window and my favorite hat with the jckbbt logo. It brought wonderful memories of my friend Brendan, who'd founded a retreat center in Sedona, Arizona.

Trey walked from the hangar, his eyes scanning the surroundings constantly. "Good morning, Ms. Windermere. Ms. Mitchell is on the plane; we'll be wheels up at 0 seven hundred. Can I get you anything?"

"Good morning, Trey. No thank you, I'm good." He nodded.

Atop the steps, I turned into the luxurious cabin of the plane where tan leather seats and couches were surrounded by dark, glossy wood. Natalie sat in a window seat, staring out to the hills. "Good morning, Natalie," I said.

She turned, her face tired, her eyes void of the normal energy I'd experienced with her. "I suppose one could say that. Hello, Sammy." I smiled slightly, acknowledging the first time she'd called me by my first name. "Leave your bag there, Trey will get it." She pointed to a seat across the aisle from her.

"I don't know how to explain this; something happened. I don't think I really slept at all, I was pouring over the many articles about me and Ollopa, trying to prove that Diana was wrong with her allegations about my motivations and interests." She paused, her fingers fiddling with the drawstrings on her emerald hoodie. "And I slowly realized I couldn't."

She called to Trey and asked him to get her a pillow. "I'm too tired to talk about it now. I'm going to take a nap. I need my wits about me for the meeting this morning."

Natalie dozed on and off during the short flight. Trey sat in the back of the plane reading a novel about a boy wizard, and I sat pondering what Natalie would say and do when she visited her attorney. The plane dropped down between the mountains of Phoenix, then a black limo whisked us away to a beautiful resort at the base of Camelback Mountain that wasn't far from her attorney's office.

In the lobby, Natalie let me know she was going to her room to rest and think, and was going to push the meeting with her attorney back until tomorrow. "I hope you can stay over an extra day. If not, my pilot can take you back to Montecito. I've got to figure this out. Trey will be in touch."

"I can stay. I'm going to hold you to having a third meeting with me."

"Fine." She turned to leave.

"Natalie—" I lowered my voice as I moved very close to her. "Why don't you talk to Matthew?"

Her eyes squinted, and head turned sideways, "Matthew? He's dead."

"Yes, true, and his Spirit is nearby . . . trust me Natalie, there's a fine line between here and there," I replied, waving my hand to the open doors of the lobby.

"And you think . . . " Natalie took a deep breath, looked out the doors and back to me, "you think his Spirit will give me my answer?"

I placed my hands on her shoulders. "No, the answer is within you now. Talking with Matthew will just let it come to the surface."

I took my room key from Trey and headed down the hall.

I heard nothing all day until Trey appeared at my door late that afternoon. "Ms. Mitchell is gone, no one has seen her on property."

"Trey you have to trust me on this." He clenched his jaw. "Trust me. Natalie is fine, and I'm pretty sure I know where she is. I'll text you when I catch up with her." He reluctantly agreed.

Natalie Looks in the Mirror

After about 20 minutes of walking, I caught site of Natalie coming down Camelback Mountain. I took a seat on a bench at the trailhead, texted Trey, and waited. She smiled as she approached, then sat down next to me.

A few minutes passed before she said, "You're right." I turned to her. "There is a fine line between here and there." She said, slowly sweeping her palm to the desert far below us.

"Come with me," I said, taking her hand and pulling her to her feet. "It's time for our third meeting."

She followed me as I took an unmarked trail around a corner. The large boulders we crossed were slanted, so we crouched to keep our balance. Natalie smiled as a cave came into view. It was the size of a small room, plenty tall enough to stand, with openings on two sides.

"Wow," she said, staring out across the neighborhoods of Scottsdale far below.

"Yes, I agree. It's one of my favorite spots on the mountain."

"You've been here before."

"Oh yeah, many times."

"You know when I texted you and said someone has to pay?" I nodded. "Well, I figured it out." Natalie's eyes filled, "Matthew helped me."

She gazed out, and continued. "I hardly slept last night; my mind raced to disprove what Diana said. I realized she was right. And the people she has poised to take over are really wonderful businesspeople . . . just really good people who want to help. One is the president of a hedge fund who lost his wife to a horrible disease. There's a tech tycoon whose son suffers from a neurological disorder, and a billionaire banker from North Dakota who himself was saved through an innovative cardiac surgical approach pioneered at Ollopa. They are all highly committed to support research on how to prevent and treat or even cure conditions like these."

Natalie let out a sad sigh. "How could I have gone so wrong? Gotten so full of myself.?"

"Yes, ego can be a powerful force . . . sometimes not such a good one."

Natalie nodded, "Why does this happen?"

"Not sure exactly," I offered, "just seems like you got distracted, and made things more about what you wanted, what you needed. I wouldn't beat yourself up over it. Your ego is just your sense of self-esteem or self-importance."

"Yes, that's it. I developed an inflated sense of self-importance." She said, shaking her head.

"You know what I call it when this happens? *Ego*, and each letter stands for a word."

Natalie moved to the stone bench at the back of the cave, a smirk on her face. "And what does it stand for?"

I said this slowly, "Energy . . . gone . . . obnoxious."

She was silent.

"Hmmmm." I teased her a bit.

"Hmmmm, what?" Natalie responded. "I know Sammy, I know. Most of the shit in the shows was because of me . . . my obnoxiousness, if that's even a word. I changed with my success . . . " Tears filled her eyes, "and now I'm ready to change back."

I pulled a piece of chalk from my pocket. "You up for a little lesson?" She looked at the chalk and the large red rock wall next to me.

"You're not serious."

"100%." I said and began to write the word transition, leaving a space between the "s" and "i" in the middle. I had Natalie close her eyes then added the "h." She laughed when I asked her to open them again, and we discussed the powerful self-reflection available when we work to take the "h" out. I had a strong sense of the "h" word capturing Natalie's' beliefs and mindset about the takeover but she had to discover the "h" for herself.

Natalie came up with a few "h" words that I wrote on the cave wall, although she shook her head, not satisfied. "Any suggestions?"

"Maybe one," I said. "Take a look at the text you sent me last night."

She pulled her phone from the small pack around her waist and tapped and swiped the screen. She stood and took the chalk from my hand and wrote the words "hanging on." "I'm hanging on tightly to everything that I have, fighting against anyone wanting to take anything from me."

"Why do you think that is?"

"I told you yesterday that I wasn't afraid of anything. But last night I realized that I am afraid of one thing . . . of what will happen to me if I left. I'm not sure who I'd be if I don't have Ollopa."

"But now you're willing to stop hanging on?" I asked. "What would replace it?"

"Um, I don't know."

"There's a great story you may like," I said. She turned to me. "The Stoic philosopher, Epictetus, tells of another philosopher named Agrippinus, who was known for his ability to do what was right. He received some awful news one morning during Nero's reign: He was exiled, to be effective immediately."

"Sounds familiar. What did he say?"

"He had a classic response. 'Very well,' he said, 'we shall take our lunch in Aricia.'"

"Bingo," she said. "I realized last night and today that when I . . . when we . . . were growing the company, there were many times things happened that were bad and difficult, and a struggle, and we just got through them. We acknowledged the facts, the not-so-good facts, then we got a clear vision of where we were headed, and we got after it . . . we made it happen."

Natalie's face took on a reflective look as she turned away. "So, he just took the news, and moved on. Right. I remember a guy giving a talk on succession planning once say, 'The best thing about moving on, is knowing when to move on.' At first when he said it, I thought how can he use the word 'best'? I thought he should have used 'difficult'. Now I'm seeing what he meant. I'm not sure why it has stuck with me all these years."

She stood and took a deep breath, "I suppose for me now, it's about going from hanging on . . . to moving on. Let's go, I have to get ready for my meeting tomorrow morning."

Learning to Trust the Future

I spent the night alone at the hotel, knowing Natalie was in full preparation mode for the meeting with her attorney. In the morning I was enjoying some coffee on my patio, watching the sun's glow begin to rise over the mountains when a text from Natalie arrived:

> Natalie: Meet me in the lobby at 8:00. I'd like you to be at the meeting. I figured out how to make her pay.

I let her know I'd be ready and pondered about what would take place at the meeting.

Natalie's attorney was younger than I expected. His head was shaved, and he wore jeans and a pressed white dress shirt. She introduced me to him as her business colleague. His office was decorated with desert art, and a picture of him with a woman and two young girls sat prominently on the credenza behind his desk. His tone was intense and focused when he spoke.

The three of us sat at the wooden conference table facing the vast desert. Natalie began, "Trevor, you know what has been happening at Ollopa, and how Diana and her team are working to take over." He nodded, a pen and legal pad on the table in front of him. "And you know I've been saying 'she is going to pay.'" Trevor's eyes remained focused on Natalie. "Well," she said, "She is going to pay." She paused, "The only thing is that the 'she' is me." Natalie was silent, letting her last statement linger.

"What do you mean?" Trevor asked, a confused look on his face.

"What I mean is, I'd like you to accept their offer. I want you to get in touch with Diana when we leave and put the deal together."

"But Natalie, if we go ahead with this, you stand to lose a lot."

Natalie stood and moved to place her hand on Trevor's shoulder, "Yes, that's what I was thinking as well. Although, recently," Natalie smiled at me, "I've come to realize I need to pay for having lost may way, having lost my integrity, and who I am as a leader, as a businesswoman." She looked back to Trevor. "Now, I've realized when we do this deal, I win."

"Are you sure? You've been fighting this takeover for months."

"I'm certain that this is the right move and what's best for the business . . . and for me," she replied.

"I'm not sure I fully understand but I'll do as you ask," he said. "I trust your judgment."

Trey was waiting out front and drove us back to the hotel where we enjoyed a wonderful lunch on the patio near the pool. Laughter and sounds of splashing filled the air.

"I feel so good, so . . . what word am I looking for?" Natalie took a sip of juice. "I feel so right. Now I suppose I just need to figure out what to do next. I cannot sit by the pool all day or take up golf or tennis. No, I need something. Years ago, I had an idea about an organization to support, encourage, and love inner city children, and I believe now is the time to get that going. My hope is we'll do great things." She turned to me, "What do you think, Sammy?"

I pulled my sunglasses up onto my head, squinting at Natalie, "A friend of mine wrote a book called, *Trust Your Animal Instincts*, and in it she shares her journey during a difficult time in her life. She was in a remote part of Costa Rica, and during her time there she worked to see what lesson, what growth, she could experience because of the different animals that were showing up around her. She wrote that one animal, the bat, does not land, it merely attaches itself to the top of the cave."

Natalie said, "So how does it take off again?"

"It doesn't." I reached across the table, placing my hand on hers, "It just lets go . . . and trusts."

— 6 —

Jess

"You don't have to control your thoughts.
You just have to stop letting them control you."

— Dan Millman

Jess on Full Court

A rush of warm air welcomed me as I entered the loud high school gym where I was to meet Jess, a senior star player from South Florida, and highly sought after by many Division 1 women's college basketball programs. I had looked at her social media accounts after Ben, a college coach I know, told me about Jess. She'd called him after he'd made contact, asking him for advice.

"It turns out she wasn't looking for tips on how to improve her jump shot," Ben had told me. "She was looking for someone she could talk to about her life. And I thought of you."

"And her parents said it was OK for me to talk with her?" I'd asked.

"She's 18, and she asked me not to involve her parents. I had to respect her wishes. And I think once you meet them, you'll know why she made that request."

So here I was on a Tuesday night watching the young woman, her ponytail flowing behind her, move easily around the court, scoring seemingly at will, and handling the ball as if connected to her by some magical force. She stole the ball twice from her opponents in the first few minutes of the game, and made a few passes—one behind her back—that caused the spectators to let out a "whoa" in unison. As I sat in the front row of the bleachers across from the teams, I noticed a woman to my right at mid-court kneeling and constantly yelling instructions to the players . . . or, as I watched more closely, just Jess.

Jess' team won the game by 24 points and Jess scored 30. As the players disappeared into the locker rooms, and the gym emptied out, a small group of men and women assembled near the locker room exit for Jess' team. Their clothing all bore the logos of colleges and universities. A few of them grabbed their phones and moved away from the group as the woman who'd been kneeling at mid-court walked quickly toward them. My college coach friend, Ben, was one who'd moved away from the group. He glanced around, noticed me standing against the wall, waved, and walked toward me. We'd known one another a long time ago. He also knew my boss, and we'd agreed to get together at this game, and see if he could introduce me to Jess.

We met at mid-court, greeting one another with a hug. While he'd told me about Jess and her tremendous talent, he also confided in me he believed she could use a little "Sammy-time"—as he called it.

"Hey Sammy," he said, turning to look at his fellow coaches. The woman from mid-court was now in the middle of the small crowd, arms crossed, talking, and turning to the coaches and recruiters. "That's Jess' mom, Amber. She's a real piece of work, a very, very good player back in her day, all-American at Tennessee." He sighed deeply. "Not sure if she realizes it's Jess we're recruiting, and not her."

I nodded slowly; my gaze focused on Amber. "Is Jess' dad around?"

He nodded slightly to the other corner of the gym where I saw a man, wearing Jess' high school colors, seated with a few other men. "That's Jess' dad, Peter. The two men with him are the athletic director from the school and Jess' coach from the traveling team she's played on for a few years. I've talked with him briefly a few times, seems like a good dad just wanting the best for his daughter."

"How about her mom?"

He just rolled his eyes, "I'll let you answer that one yourself."

"Is she really one of the top 5 high school recruits, as the articles I read say?"

"Number one as far as I'm concerned."

"And Jess knows I'm coming?"

"Yes, I told her I'd be bringing someone with me who could help her. Given that her folks are here, I don't know how open she'll be, but I agreed to do the introductions right after the game. Remember though, that her mom and dad don't know why you're here."

We turned as voices and laughter filled the gym as players came from the locker room. Jess walked alone, wearing sweats and white socks with sandals, and her bright yellow headband still in place. She went to her dad for a quick hug, sliding her backpack off her shoulder and into his hand, then turned and walked toward her mom and the coaches. There was no hug from her mom, just a fist bump, as they turned and leaned against the stage at the end of the gym. One by one, Amber called the coaches over, her arms remaining crossed as the coaches spoke with her and Jess. She'd shake their hands when she was done with them, and call over the next one. We'd made our way to them, and were the last to meet.

"Hi, Amber. Hi, Jess, nice game," Ben said. "This is my friend, Sammy." Jess extended her hand, and we shook.

"Nice game?" Amber said, emphasizing the word nice. "Jess was amazing, she could have scored 50 if she wanted to."

"Mom, it's good, we won," Jess said in an apologetic tone.

"Yes, and so did all the teams of the other top recruits, and I know of two of them went for over 40 points." She looked to me. "You a coach too?"

I nodded. "I guess you could say that, although I don't coach basketball."

"Then what do you coach?" Amber asked, intensity on your face.

"I coach people, with their lives. You know, supporting them to move from where they are to where they want to be."

"Oh, got it, one off those life coach people," she said with a slight roll of her eyes.

"Well." Ben said, "I just wanted to say hello, congratulate you as you head into the playoffs, and let you know we are very interested in having you visit our school and talk with you about the possibility of a wonderful education and career there."

"Yeah, yeah, yeah, we know," said Amber as she began walking away. "Just watch what she's gonna do in states. She may just skip college and go straight to the WNBA."

Jess lingered behind as her mom crossed the court. She looked at Ben. "This is the woman you told me about?"

"Yes. I'm sure Sammy can help you."

Jess turned to me. "Can you meet me at a gym not far from here, Saturday morning? Early. I practice by myself at 6am. Coach Ben can send you the address."

"I'll be there," I said. Jess gave me a sad smile as she walked beside her dad, seemingly not concerned with catching up to her mom.

In the parking lot Ben said, "Thanks for coming Sammy, there's something I want you to know." I leaned in, pursing my lips. "Most of the recruits have already committed to their schools, it's not common for a player like Jess to have not made a decision yet. Most of us think it's because Amber loves the attention this recruiting process brings.

I nodded. "Yes, I could see that."

"Last year in the semi-finals of the state playoffs, Jess left the game early and her team lost. The reason given was a nagging foot injury, although most of us now know it was not that, but rather Jess' anxiety that caused her to leave the game."

"Hmmm, really?" I said. Ben nodded. "How was she this year?"

"Well, there were only two games this year where the foot flared up." My friend said, holding his fingers in quotation marks when he said the word foot. "I just know that one of Jess' best friends, Tai, a girl who plays for a school in the next town over and has played travel ball with her for years, and is coming to play for us next year is really worried about Jess. She keeps me up to date on what's happening."

"How do you think she'll do in the playoffs?"

"Not sure." He raised his brow as we hugged and said goodbye.

JUST ONE MISSED SHOT

The sun was climbing over the horizon Saturday morning as I pulled into the empty lot next to the gym Ben had told me about, and parked in the far corner. Six o'clock came and went and just when I was ready to leave, I saw a car pull in and park next to the back door. Jess got out, and grabbed a key from her pocket. She saw me climbing out of my car, waved, and pointed to the gym door.

"Thanks for coming Sammy," she said. "Sorry about this cloak-and-dagger stuff, but you saw my mom the other night. I've learned it's better to go around her sometimes."

"I understand. I won't say a word to anyone about our meeting unless you want me to."

She studied me for a moment. Then she motioned for me to follow her through the door. She set down her gym bag, put on her shoes, grabbed a ball, and began dribbling down the court. I stayed on the sideline.

Jess made a free throw, then flipped the ball high toward half court and ran to catch up with it, grabbed it with one hand and began dribbling down court, making lighting quick moves against imaginary defenders, and always ending with the ball going through the hoop. Then she went to the foul line at that end of the court and completed the process over . . . and over . . . and over again. I watched, now convinced Ben was probably right about her being the number one player in the country.

After about 30 minutes, Jess grabbed her water bottle and took a seat next to me.

"I . . . uh . . . I'm not really sure how to begin," she said. "And I'm not—

"Jess," I interrupted, "I know about your foot injury."

Staring straight ahead, she asked, "What do you know about that?"

"Well, I've heard it's not your foot at all. It's your head."

Jess looked at me, her face not showing what she thought of my very direct comment. I made the choice to get right to it with Jess, to address her anxiety, as I knew with Amber hovering around, I might not get another chance. "Are you a therapist? I mean, are you sworn to keep anything I tell you confidential?"

"I'm not a licensed therapist, although I do support people in sorting through whatever is going on in their lives." I paused, causing Jess to look to me. "But I will swear on a Bible if you want me to, that nothing you tell me will go any further unless you give me explicit permission to share it." I paused, Jess looking to me cautiously.

Jess stood. "Will you rebound for me?"

"Sure." I followed her, taking my place under the net as Jess began sinking one free throw after another. She began talking as we continued our shoot and rebound drill.

"It began when I was young. I was about ten years old, and I was playing in a championship game in a summer league. It was the end of the game, and we were down by two. I brought the ball up and passed to a teammate, then drifted to the corner behind the 3-point line. My teammate drove down the lane and passed it to me where I squared up and drained what I thought was a 3 to win the game. Turns out I'd moved slightly closer to the basket and my foot was on the line, so we only tied the game and headed into overtime. I remember my mom, who was the coach then, too, hurrying to meet me as I made my way to the bench. 'Jess,' she was screaming, holding my shoulders. 'You have to know where you are on the court, this game should be over.'"

Jess paused. "I was friggin' ten years old," she whispered. Then, in her normal voice, she resumed her story. "The gym became quiet;

everyone looking at me and my mom. One referee leaned in and said something to the coach of the opposing team. My mom shook her head, and turned with her clipboard and knelt in front of my teammates sitting on the bench. I took a seat next to them, my heart beating faster and harder than ever, knocking hard against my chest like a fist pounding on a door. I couldn't catch my breath, and I was in really good shape for a kid. It was the first time I had that feeling."

She stood and paced back and forth in front of the bench a few times. "It was close during overtime, and again I had the last shot to win the game. The ball hit the front of the rim, bounced to the back, then off to the side. We lost by one. I looked over to see my mom, who just turned away. We stayed for the trophy presentation, then took a long ride home in silence. After that's when it started. I hardly slept that night, and when I did, I kept dreaming about the missed shot."

I caught the ball as it swished through the net, not touching the rim. I rolled the ball slowly toward the stands, and walked to Jess. She stood, staring at the hoop, tears filling her eyes then sliding down her cheeks.

She wiped them away, looking to me and welcoming my hug as I slowly raised my arms. "I'm just so scared, I feel so helpless. It's like I used to worry just about basketball back then, now I worry about everything, I just don't know what to do."

Heavy Burdens for Young Shoulders

We took a seat in the circle at the center of the court, both crossing our legs at our ankles. Jess told me the path to the state championship was to win four games . . . in a row; lose, and your season is over. The first game was Friday, then Wednesday, then Friday, and championship a week later on Saturday afternoon.

"Can you do it?" I asked.

"Don't know. And it's not just me, gotta be 'we.'" Jess untied her sneakers and pulled them off. I remained silent, glancing toward the bleachers where Jess' bag sat next to the ball, and trusting the silence of the gym to pull something from her. Finally, Jess took a few deep breaths, "I guess the best way to sum it all up Sammy, is—" she paused, "I just worry about everything. My grades. What college I'll go to. Whether I'll screw up and the scholarship offers will dry up. How I will play there. How my dad will be when I'm away. My weight. How hard it is to have a normal life—or what I think a normal life might be. Everything, it's exhausting." I nodded gently. "And of course, I worry about my mom, and what she's gonna do or say." She stood, raising her arms over her head for a good stretch. "And it's just not me. I have a lot of friends with this thing they call anxiety. Some go to therapists, some take meds . . . one kid from a town over took his life last year. I'm just scared, and I feel so helpless."

"I know Jess, I know. And it's okay, you can learn to deal with, and overcome, the times when this feeling of worry, of nervousness about what will happen in your life, of the uncertainty of life presents itself."

"I wish I could. I've talked with doctors, even took some pills for a little while, but my mom wants me too just, 'be strong.' She says, 'You don't need to talk with anyone, what would it do to your recruiting if they knew you were doing this?'" Jess stood, shook her head, and walked to get her bag.

"How do you feel about that?"

She put her sneakers in the bag, slipped on her sandals, took a few gulps from her water bottle, and smiled sadly. "Honestly Sammy, I don't know. I just don't know. I need some help. I really need some help." She said, emphasizing the word really. "Can I give you my number, and maybe we can stay in touch? Or I can call you once in a while?" She pulled her backpack on, and we began walking to the door. "It's weird how you just showed up, but there's something about you that makes me feel just a little better, like it just might all be okay."

"It will be okay Jess, and sure, call my number now, so we're connected. Let's talk again soon." I held my phone to Jess so she could see my number and when my phone buzzed from her calling, I hit the button to take the call. "Hi, Sammy here. Who's calling please?" Jess put the phone to her ear.

"Ha ha, it's me." She disconnected our call as we began walking to the door.

"Jess," I said, putting my arm on her shoulder, "anxiety, and depression are a serious struggle, and there are many people who should seek professional support . . . you know doctors, and medication where needed." She nodded. "This said, there are some other things you can begin doing that will help you with . . ." Just then the door opened, and Amber walked through, stopping to look at me, then Jess, then back to me.

"What the hell's going on here?" She looked at Jess. "You're supposed to be here alone, do you want to screw this up by getting in some kind of trouble?"

She turned to me, "And you, whoever you are. Jess does not need some crazy-ass life coach. She doesn't need anyone. She's got me and we're gonna make sure she gets into whatever school is going to give her the best shot at a few national championships, then the pros. Stay away from my daughter." She shook her head, grabbed Jess' arm and said, "Come on Jess, let's go. You have a game in a few days."

Jess pulled away, "No Mom, no. You just can't keep running my life. I'm not sure why Sammy's here, all I can tell you is I need somebody right now, someone to help me get through this."

"But Jess," her mom said, "I . . ."

Jess cut her off, tears coming, and her voice raised. "No Mom, no. I'll be nineteen in a month; do you realize that? Nineteen. None of my other teammates are that old. You . . . you had to start me late—taking me away from my best friends when I was young, and then even holding me back in third grade. Third grade, Mom. What mom holds her intelligent, socially interactive daughter back to repeat third grade?

"But Jess, I did it . . ." Amber began to reply until Jess screamed.

"Stop, be quiet. I know why you did it. So I'd be bigger and stronger when the colleges came calling." Jess shook her head, her hands clenched at her side. "Do you have any idea . . . any clue, how many times I've thought about quitting basketball? Do you even have a clue as to some other thoughts I've had that are way worse?" Jess let that comment settle, then stepped aside her mom. "No, I'm sure you don't. Maybe your plan backfired about keeping me back, because I'm over 18 now and I can talk to whoever I want, and you cannot stop me. I'm outta here." Jess ran through the door, and the sound of squealing tires entered the gym. Amber looked at me with disgust and exited the gym.

Jess' first game Friday night was in her home gym. Amber was there at mid-court, naturally, seemingly unaffected by Jess' outburst on Saturday morning. Jess looked tense, not having her best game, although still scoring 22 and her team winning easily. We talked once before the next game. Jess told me she had not spoken with her mom at all since Saturday. She said her mom was telling her about the teams, and how Jess had to score a lot of points. She said she just listened, then walked away.

I met Ben for a bite to eat, then we went to the second game together. The gym was packed, and again Jess did not look like herself. She missed her first 7 shots, and her team fell behind by 12 points. Her mother, naturally, kept screaming instructions at her.

As the teams were warming up for the second half, Jess dribbled over toward me and Ben, looking to me as she bounced the ball between her legs. I pulled my hands up as I took a deep breath, signaling her to do the same as I mouthed the word "Relax" to her. Jess came out and hit two 3-pointers and her team seemed to follow her lead as they turned the momentum, winning the game by 11 points.

The third playoff game Friday night is when it happened. I got a few texts from Jess the day of the game, and she was not feeling good. The game was against the team that her best friend, Tai, played for, and was at a neutral site where this game and the championship would be played. She said she'd be okay, and declined my offer to meet for a bite to eat.

> Me: hey Jess, sending good energy for your strong leadership and focus

> Jess: thanks Sammy, most people usually just text me 'good luck'

Me: ha ha, yes, just remember though, I'm a crazy-ass life coach according to your mom . . . and OK . . . good luck

Jess: I have a feeling I'm gonna need more than luck

The semi-final game was one of offensive runs. Tai had 18 in the first half, and Jess 16. Both teams were shooting a high percentage. In the 3rd quarter, with the game tied, Jess missed a short jumper from the corner and then missed three more. I could only guess her head raged with thoughts of failure. I wanted to run onto the court and give her a hug. Knowing this was not possible, I sat, watching Jess' team fall behind by 6 points, until the fans all stood in unison with a gasp as Jess dove for a loose ball going out of bounds; she hit the ground hard and stayed down. Her coach and trainer hurried to kneel next to Jess, leaning down to hear what Jess was saying. Jess sat up, pulled her knees to her chest, rocked back and forth, staring straight ahead. I'd seen this pose many times, and it was not that of a foot injury, it was that of a hurting young woman. After a few minutes, she stood, favoring her foot, and limped off the court, her arms around the trainer and a teammate.

The game resumed, but my focus was on Jess, who sat near the end of the bench, holding an ice pack on her foot, her sneaker laying nearby. She looked at me quickly then turned away. The game looked like it was going to be won by Tai's team, as Jess' friend approached the 40-point mark. With just over a minute left, Jess' teammates forced a few turnovers and made consecutive 3-pointers to pull within 2 points. With just seconds left Tai uncharacteristically dribbled the ball off her foot as she attempted to run the final seconds down off the clock. The ball bounced to Jess' teammate, who turned toward her basket, took two dribbles, and launched the ball from over half-court. The ball hung in the air for what seemed like minutes, the crowd stood, and the ball swished through the net as the final horn sounded. Jess' team had miraculously won the game, and were headed to the State Championship. Jess limped toward the celebration wearing a somber look on her face.

Jess again came from the locker room, meeting her Dad and exiting the gym. She glanced to me, shaking her head slightly in sadness. Amber hardly noticed Jess as she did her usual post-game thing.

About midnight my phone lit up with a text from Ben.

Ben: thought you'd want to see this, for your eyes only

The little bubbles showed on my phone, indicating Ben was sending something else. The photo that popped up on my phone caused my heart to drop. It was Jess, kneeling at a toilet, her arms wrapped around it, and Tai next to her holding her ponytail.

I began to text back, then just touched my phone to call Ben.

"Hey," he answered. "I . . ."

I interrupted. "What happened? Is she okay? Where is she?"

"Slow down, Sammy, slow down. Jess is okay. She's at Tai's house, and this picture was taken by Tai, nobody else will see it. She's with her."

"What happened?"

"Well, best I can gather, is some of Tai's teammates got together to have a few drinks after their loss, and end of season. And it being a Friday night I guess the party got bigger than expected. Tai said she'd texted Jess, and was thinking Jess would go home, since she knew Jess would try to do her Saturday morning workout if her foot felt okay. She was surprised when Jess showed up, and began drinking a lot, and doing some shots."

"Oh, shit."

"Yes. You can say that again."

"OK, please keep me posted. I'm gonna go to the gym in the morning and see if Jess shows up."

"Sounds good." Ben said. "And Sammy, thanks again for anything you can do to help."

"Sure." I said as I touched my phone to end the call. I'm not sure if Ben talking to Tai, then to me, violated any recruiting rules, and I really didn't care.

This time when I pulled into the gym lot, I backed in next to the door, so I could keep an eye out for Jess. The sun was climbing into the sky, and felt good on my face since I'd dropped the top down for the ride. I got out of my car and leaned on the hood, watching for a few minutes until I smiled slightly when Jess' car pulled in.

Jess got out, pulling her backpack from the passenger seat. Her hair was in a ponytail, held back by her trademark bright yellow headband. She did not smile, and the dark circles under her eyes looked like she was an outfielder in a baseball game.

"Nice car." She said.

"Thanks. How are you?"

"How do I look?"

"Not real good."

"You can say that again. Probably don't smell so great either"

Jess walked toward the door. "Can I come in?" I asked.

"If you want, but I'll tell you now, it's not gonna be pretty."

"I'm okay with that."

I took a seat on the first row of the bleachers as Jess sipped Gatorade and laced up her sneakers. She stretched for a few minutes then headed to the foul line to shoot, then begin her full court workout. She missed the first 4 shots she took, shook her head, and ran into the bathroom. The sounds of gagging and coughing echoed through the empty gym.

Saying Goodbye to Mr. Nasty

Jess came back out and began again. As she stood at the foul line, her back to me, I jogged to mid-court. She made the shot and flipped the ball high in the air toward me. I caught it, and held it on my hip as Jess stopped running and walked to me. I rolled the ball toward the sideline as she collapsed in my arms, her tears coming and sobs filling the gym, and the smell of liquor filling the air. After a few minutes, I pulled away gently, as Jess pulled her shirt to dry her tears.

"How about you stop now? And we just talk?" I asked, bending down to sit in the circle at half-court. Jess did the same. On the way into the gym, I'd noticed a coach's small whiteboard with a marker on the bleachers. "Stay here, I want to show you something." I grabbed the board and returned quickly.

"Oh no, you're not going to show me any plays or anything?" Jess said.

I smiled. "No, no plays."

I wrote the word transition on the board, leaving the space between the "s" and "i." I asked her what she saw, and like the others, she said the word and inquired about the empty space. I had her close her eyes, added the "h" and then asked her to read the new word. She did, laughing softly as she continued to wipe her eyes.

We talked about the transhition she was in—a big one—of moving from high school to college. Jess said she understood this new word, transhition, and it reminded her of another word to describe her situation: shitshow.

I laughed. "Oh, yes, I know that one well." I paused. "Jess, can I offer you some things to consider about where you are? And perhaps some strategy to help you move through this 'foot' injury?" She nodded, pulling her headband down to her nose, then back up.

"The key to moving through your shitshow is to take the shit out of the show." Jess laughed, saying she liked that line. "Yes, a lot of people do. What you may want to do is break that word down into two words . . . shit . . . and show. The show is life, it's the facts you have to deal with, the pressure, being a teenager, this recruitment process, the championship game, and—"

"And a crazy mom." Jess interrupted in a sad tone.

"Yes, and a crazy mom. This is the show, and you're going to have many more challenging times in your life. You don't want to walk around like doom and gloom all the time, you just have to know they will come. The shit, on the other hand, is simply how you deal with these facts, how you navigate life's challenges." Jess was nodding.

"But besides doctors and medications, what can I do? I've had some tests done and my levels all seem to be good . . . you know, when they check your blood and all that." I nodded. "When the thoughts come, I just feel helpless."

"Yep, got it, been there myself. So, what if you're able to acknowledge the thoughts, then replace them with other ones, with more useful thoughts?"

"That sounds great in theory—" she said, a note of skepticism in her voice.

"Well, let's start with this." I held the marker to her and told her to put an X through the "h." She did, and I asked, "Now since you removed the 'h,' think of a word that begins with 'h' that you could also get rid of." I let her sit for a moment, her mind racing. "You've used it a lot when we've talked. You just said it a minute ago." She turned to me, our eyes locked on one another, I began slowly, "I just feel so . . . ." I stopped as Jess completed the sentence.

"Helpless."

"Yes. Helpless. That feeling of not knowing what to do, of thinking there is nothing you can do." She nodded, reaching down to untie her sneakers. "How about I offer you a few things you can begin doing, some things to experiment with to move you from your anxious thoughts, to more useful ones?"

"Sounds good."

I grabbed Jess' hand and pulled her up as we both stood. I stared at her in silence, then asked, "What if you lose the championship game?"

She shook her head, "Now why would I want to think about that when you said I should hold useful thoughts? Why would you ask that question?"

"Okay. What were you thinking about last night before you went to the party, and what were you thinking when you started doing shots?"

Her eyes filled, she looked away, then slowly back to me, "I was thinking what will happen if we lose."

"Right, and that's okay. Remember, you will have shitty thoughts, most of us do, it's part of being human. Our brain wants to keep us safe and protected, so it will always look for things that can hurt us, like losing the championship game. Let's play this out." I paused, "Jess, what will happen if you lose the championship?"

"My mom will freak."

"Yes, probably. And what else?"

Jess was silent, shaking her head, "I don't know."

"OK, how about what I once heard that Coach who's recruiting you, you know the one they just call The Legend, say in an interview. He said he tells his players, if you lose, you're still going to have your family, still going to have your friends, and you're not going to lose your scholarship. Life will go on for you, and you'll go on to win some more games, and lose some."

Jess took a deep breath, letting this sink in. "Yeah, I guess."

"Yeah. So why not hold useful thoughts about the game and preparing to the best of your ability, and being thankful for the opportunity to play in the championship."

"I see what you're saying, go down the negative road, play it out, and then realize that even if the outcome is not what we sought, it's still okay."

I nodded as she continued, "But still, losing would suck."

I lifted my brow, and tilted my head, "Compared to what?"

Jess looked confused, "Compared to what? What?"

"Take a minute, and think about something worse than losing a game. Think of illness and disease and sick kids, of financial hardships, of other real-life struggles people are facing."

She was nodding, "See, Jess, asking 'Compared to what?' is a great tool to shift your perspective, to see your challenges as just those; challenges you'll face and figure out how to get through. The thing is you need to first catch your negative thinking. It's just a habit you've created, and you must really heighten your awareness to catch these thoughts so you can work to change them to more positive ones."

"OK, I got it, that makes sense. Anything else?"

"Yes, you can name your negative thinking habit, you can name your anxiety. Make up this character that is the voice in your head. What would you call him . . . or her?"

Jess laughed, "Nasty. Yes, Nasty just popped into my head."

"I like it. So when Nasty shows up, you can say something like, 'Oh, hey Nasty, it's you again. I figured you'd show up. But here's the thing, I'm good, you can get out of here. Bye Nasty.'"

Jess was smiling now, the stress gone from her face. I told her to try it, to say these words our loud. She did, and kept smiling.

"You see, Jess, when you do this, you realize you are *not* your thoughts, you are the thinker of them, and this is the most powerful thing we all have available to us . . . the ability to choose our thinking—the voice in our head—in any circumstance. Now after you say hi and bye to Nasty, do this, take three deep breaths. Breathe in and on the exhale say slowly, "I'm good', then take another deep breath and on the exhale say slowly, 'with', and then one final deep breath, and on the exhale say slowly, 'my life."

I had Jess do this a few times, with her head up and shoulders back. I had her take really full, deep breaths. After the third time, she asked, "Can I add one more line?"

"Sure."

Jess closed her eyes, took a deep breath, and on the exhale her mouth moved slightly, "I got this."

"I like it, and yes, you do. You do got this . . . and anything else that comes down the road. Jess, take care of you." I put my hands on her shoulders, "Take care of you. There's a great quote by Wilma Rudolph, a woman who overcame brutal poverty and physical challenges to become an Olympic track champion in 1956 and 1960. She said, "I loved the feeling of freedom in running, the fresh air, the feeling that the only person I'm competing with is me."

Jess gave me a hug. "Thanks Sammy, I know this is still going to take some time; for me to work through this, and build new habits, and I will. I now feel like I can start to move from helpless to more in control."

"Yes, you can. It's not about not having the Nasty thoughts; it's about not letting them win." Jess grabbed her bag and we walked out the door, her arm over my shoulders.

The sunlight and a blast of heat welcomed us as we left the gym. "Oh no, here she comes," said Jess as we both watched Amber's car come quickly toward us.

She screeched to a stop, jumping out quickly, and coming to me, "I told you to stay away. What don't you understand?" I began to reply and stopped when Jess spoke.

"If I were her, I'd say I don't understand you?" Amber looked confused, as Jess continued, "If I were her, I'd say I can't understand how a mom who says she wants the best for her daughter acts in such a way that produces just the opposite."

Amber stood, her shoulders slumped, her tired face just looking to Jess, then to me.

Jess walked to her mom, "I don't want you at the game Saturday. Just stay home and watch it on TV. I love you, Mom, and I want our love to grow stronger, and if you want that too, just watch the game from home." Jess got in her car and drove away. Part of me wanted to say something to Amber, I didn't. I felt sad for her, standing alone in the parking lot with tears in her eyes. I drove away.

Jess and I texted and spoke a few times as Saturday approached. She said she was feeling pretty good, and while Nasty was still showing up, he and her feelings of helplessness were not staying around too long. Ben and I met for dinner before the game. The arena was packed, with many coaches now filling the front row, even The Legend was there.

Jess looked over and gave me a wink as she made her way to half-court for the opening tip, showing no signs of a nagging foot injury. The first half was well-played, with the teams exchanging the lead multiple times. At half, Jess' team was down by 1 point. I was not sure if Amber would show or not, and up until now I did not see—or hear—her. Jess' Dad sat alone on the opposite side, rolling and unrolling the game program nervously. Jess looked to him at the start of the second half, smiling as he held up his thumb. The opposing team went on a strong run, taking a 9-point lead with only 8 minutes left. Jess' coach called time out, and I watched as Jess stood on the sideline, listening to the coach, and then taking 3 deep breaths. The team put their hands together and then broke the huddle. While Jess' teammates headed to the floor, I saw her take one final deep breath, and her mouth moved slightly on the long exhale.

Simply put, Jess took over the game. Her defense was relentless, causing turnovers and blocking two shots. On the offensive end of the court, she simply called for the ball, and scored, or passed to a teammate to score when she got double teamed. She scored 14 points in those final minutes and her team cruised to a 7-point victory.

The gym erupted at the final horn, with the players and fans celebrating and Jess giving an interview to several reporters holding their phones to her face. I waited until she came from the locker room. I met her just as her Dad was arriving. They hugged, tears in his eyes, and Jess introduced us. Jess and I hugged, exchanged goodbyes, and committing to staying in touch. As I left, I turned to see her and her Dad talking with The Legend.

The next day I was having coffee and reading an article about Jess and her team's championship season. I smiled when I got to the end and read the final quote from Jess, "I look forward to going to college and play ball, and compete for a national title. Even more, I look forward to continuing to grow stronger in dealing with the difficulties in life. I've suffered from anxiety and depression since I was 10, and I now realize it does not have the power to control me. It will show up again, of this I'm sure, and I will deal with it."

So, there's the story of how I met Jess. She's an amazing young woman. She and her mom worked hard to strengthen their relationship, and I have to say I'm quite happy with the work Amber did on herself; life's just too damn short, and too valuable to not work on building loving relationships. After all, without them, well, life's just not as fulfilling.

While The Legend wanted Jess to come play for him and his dynasty program, Jess chose a smaller school in the same conference who had struggled for many years. She told me she did not want the pressure of walking into an established champion; rather she said she'd take the pressure of working to be part of a team who builds one.

It's now been two years since I first met Jess and her underdog team is playing for the national championship against The Legend's team. I'm watching the game on TV. It's been unexpectedly tight, coming down to the final buzzer. Jess' team is behind by 2 points. She slid to the corner, settling in behind the 3-point line, and taking a pass from her teammate, rises up in one fluid motion to release a 3-pointer.

I know what you're thinking. *Did it go in?*

Does it really matter?

Jess texted me just this morning about this exact thing.

> Jess: So now, Sammy, I just shoot. Some go in and some don't. I always hold the thought of making my shots, and I'm okay when I don't. It's just a game.

— 7 —

Bobby

"I have fought the good fight,
I have finished the race,
I have kept the faith."

– St. Paul

The Surgeon at the Deli

The quote by St. Paul reminds me of another client of mine, Bobby. I call him a client, although when I'm with him I feel more like he's my sage, sharing his experience and the resulting wisdom that has come from it. Oh, there are hard times for sure . . . but Bobby has managed to not let the shit take over his show. Our relationship, our beautiful relationship, reminds me of an often-used quote, "When the student is ready, the teacher appears." Bobby is my teacher.

He was able to walk and drive and feed himself when we first met at a wonderful place called the Deli on 4th in a hip town outside of Philadelphia. I'd seen a photo of Bobby, so recognized him immediately as I approached the deli. He was sitting outside at a small black metal table when I arrived. He was sipping an iced tea, legs crossed, and smiling at nothing in particular. He stood, pulling a chair out for me to join him. "Good morning, Sammy." He extended his hand. "You look just like your picture."

"Hello, Bobby. Nice to meet." I took a seat. "What a beautiful day. So great to have spring showing up."

"Yes," he said as he sat down again. "Sure was a cold, gray winter. Are you hungry? They have some great hoagies here."

"Hoagies?" I offered as a one-word question.

"Oh yeah, kind of like a little heaven here on earth for the hungry. Like sub sandwiches but better. You can get turkey, tuna, roast beef, or the classic Italian. That's got the Italian meats and cheese all stuffed into a fresh roll."

"Sounds amazing."

"Trust me, it is." He patted his belly. "Just can't eat them every day, and you have got to go with the hot peppers as well."

I followed him to the deli door, which he held open for me. Bobby ordered for both of us, and insisted on paying. I imagined his warm, calm demeanor and caring energy had benefited so many of his patients over his 25 years as a surgeon. I liked this man immediately.

We found a table inside and dug into our sandwiches, having to squeeze the roll to squish the sandwich and make it easier to eat. Bobby took a bite, wiped his mouth, but started to talk while he was chewing. "You asked how I was?" he said. I nodded. "I'm doing okay. It's been a ride for sure, lots of uncertainty about what's going on with me."

He raised two fingers to his throat, rubbing lightly on a small scar. "My initial symptoms were cramping in my left hand and weakness. I had an MRI of my neck that revealed a herniated disc. And everyone thought that was the cause, so I had an operation to fix that." He let out a deep breath and finished, "Unfortunately, there was no improvement, and things got worse."

Bobby smiled at an older man leaving the deli. "Then we began doing some other tests with several doctors, mostly eliminating what my situation wasn't. Finally, we ended up with only one item that couldn't be scratched from the list—ALS."

Silence filled the air between us though I could hear cars whizzing by on the street. People came and went through the glass door of the deli. "I'm sorry," I said, not knowing what else to say.

"Yeah, me too. Just life, I guess. Well, that's my reaction *now*. But I wasn't always so calm." He popped the final bite of the first half of his sandwich into his mouth, I noticed the small brace on two of his fingers. "Though I never got really angry. Guess that may show up as I continue on this journey. I've just thought, 'Really? This is my cross to bear?' I was 58 years old in the prime of my surgical career, the kids were out of college and on their own, and me and my wife, Trish, were ready to enjoy these years. I have given a lot of bad news to people over the years, but sharing the news about my diagnosis with my children was the toughest thing I ever did, and they were, and are, amazing."

Bobby rubbed his hands together slowly. I nodded, reinforcing his thoughts and the same thoughts shared by countless people who've received a brutal diagnosis.

"How are you now?" I asked.

He gazed reflectively into his drink, then pointed down the street to a huge stone church sitting on the corner, its cross standing strong atop the tall steeple rising into the clear blue sky. "Doing OK. I'm still working with patients and overseeing their treatments, although I no longer "operate."

"In my experience when people receive a diagnosis of an incurable, terminal disease, anger can sometimes consume them and that can be especially true with ALS because there are no effective treatments."

Bobby shook his head, "I was . . . and am . . . determined to not allow myself to get angry. There have been tough times already and I'm well aware of what this disease will do to my body. Operating on people and helping them heal was a big portion of my life's purpose, and it's incredibly hard to accept that I can no longer do that."

"But I know that I can't change the facts of what's happening, I can only control how I deal with it. Trish and I figured in times like this you can either run away from your Faith, or run to it." He stared down the street, his gaze fixing on the top of the steeple. "We decided to run to it."

We finished our lunch, then walked to sit on the front steps of the massive, stone church. I asked Bobby how I might support him on his journey. He rubbed his hands together. "You know, Sammy, I'm not really sure. I have a lot of support lined up to help me and my family in the days and months ahead—family, friends, my congregation, health-care experts, you name it. But sometimes I'd like to talk to someone who's outside of it all, you know?"

"Yes, sometimes it's easier to talk with strangers than those closest to us."

"So, I guess we can just talk when I feel like I need to. I'd also like to know that maybe other people could benefit from what I'm learning on this journey—not just about dealing with ALS but how to live life fully in the face of challenges. So maybe you could help share it with others. Sound good?"

"Perfect." I placed my hand on his shoulder.

Bobby sat up straight and smiled slightly. "I remember once going to the Delmar racetrack watching the horses with some friends and family, and that day a bunch of long shots won; you know, horses with high odds that were not favored in the race." I nodded, remembering the few times I went to Saratoga with my mom and dad. "Well," Bobby said, "my brother-in-law told me what we need to remember is the horse doesn't know his odds when he gets in the starting gate."

We stood and he turned to me. "Unfortunately, I'm not a horse, and I know the odds are not in my favor in this race. But I can't focus on my odds right now, I need to focus on one thing right now."

"And what is that one thing?"

"I'm not sure yet, but it will be a very important thing to give me a goal to focus on. I'll know it when the time is right." His strong jaw was clenched with determination.

That night I said some prayers and had Bobby at the top of the list, as I knew his adversaries—time and sickness—very well. I will always remember that first meeting with Bobby.

WILL THE WALK HAPPEN?

A few months later, summer was in full swing, and I'd passed a few pop-up stores selling fireworks for the coming 4th of July holiday. The intense humidity had overtaken the northeast states and staying dry outside was a futile effort. Bobby had texted me and asked to meet. People were moving slowly around the streets of the small village of Doylestown, ducking in and out of shops and restaurants in an effort to cool down. I saw Bobby before he saw me; his gait was slow, and his arms seemed to hang still at his side. He was no longer able to drive, as his hands and legs were getting weaker, he had gotten a ride from Trish or one of his children. He smiled at a young couple pushing a stroller, and gave me a wave when he saw me. His arms were thin, and I felt the bones of his back and shoulders as we hugged. When he pulled off his sunglasses, his eyes were bright.

"Hi, Sammy, thanks for coming. It's good to see you again."

"You too, Bobby. How about we go inside where you can cool down?" I said as I headed to the door.

He grabbed my arm. "If it's okay with you, I'd like to sit outside. The heat is actually good for my muscles." I smiled, sliding down onto a chair at one of the outdoor tables and watched Bobby do the same, though more slowly and consciously. "So how are you? Doing okay with this heat?" he asked.

My hair was up in a ponytail, and I grabbed the navy bandanna around my neck to wipe my face. "Yep, sweating away like the rest of us, right?"

He smiled. "Right."

"So, it's good for you? The heat."

"Yes, I actually take a sauna almost every day because the heat is good for my muscles. With this disease, you really must be your own best advocate. Trish and I research every day about treatment and are willing to try anything that may help."

A young waiter in RayBans, wearing white shorts and a blue T-shirt bearing the restaurant's logo of a black lab, arrived with two glasses of water and menus, and said he'd be back in a minute. "What treatments are you undergoing now?" I asked.

Bobby sat back. "Well, Sammy, great question . . . . Unfortunately, for people with ALS there are only two medicines that have been approved, and neither is a game changer. I'm thankful for my medical knowledge, which helps me understand my options when it comes to clinical trials. Trish and I made the decision to travel to South Korea where I received stem cell treatment, and I believe it helped." He paused and took a deep breath. "But, it's a long trip and very expensive, which is why most people can't do it. I also believe that good nutrition and daily physical activity are vital."

He paused and took a sip of water. "Remember I talked about the one thing I need to focus on that I'll do when the time is right?" I nodded. "Well, our only daughter is engaged now. The wedding is the end of next March." Bobby took a deep breath, his eyes intently focused on mine as a beautiful smile of determination formed on his face. "And I *will* walk her down that aisle.

"This is great news, Bobby!" I said. "You and Trish must be so excited. That's just over eight months away. How can I support you?"

"Trish and I have committed to go to Florida for some treatment to help boost my immune system. I guess just let's keep meeting when I'm in town and talking. And again, write some of what we talk about down, so you can share it with others who are—or will—have similar challenges. One thing I realized right at the start of this is I have so many people who love me and are willing to support me. I want other people to know that they should always let people know when they're experiencing tough times in life and allow others to help you. Trust me, people really need to know that they don't have to go through whatever it is they're experiencing alone."

He bit his bottom lip, as tears filled his eyes. "I knew when I married Trish how lucky I was because she is one of the most amazing people I'd ever met. And I should have done a better job of letting her know that throughout our marriage and raising the kids. Here's what I've come to realize, and appreciate about her, now more than ever. She simply does what she knows we need to do; it's funny, it's like she knows how I feel even before I do, and she always figures out a way to move forward. I worked so hard and so many hours in my career as a surgeon and I missed a lot of moments." He took a deep breath. "Now, there's nothing I take for granted, even things like getting dressed or eating or going somewhere on my own. I can guarantee I'm not going to miss anything from now on, and trust me, I will walk down that aisle with our daughter in March."

Bobby told me he was taking over 50 pills per day, and added a few drinks with protein and other beneficial powders mixed in. He's thankful for two friends who come to his home and lead him through a few strenuous workouts per week to keep him moving and his legs strong.

A car pulled up by the corner and honked. Bobby waved to the driver. "That's my ride. Thanks for talking with me. There's something about you that makes me feel calmer, and surer that it's all going be okay."

We said our goodbyes, and agreed to meet when he returned from his treatments in Florida in a month. His courage and strong commitment to keep walking inspired me, and more importantly raised my awareness and appreciation for many simple things in life that we must not take for granted.

HEART ATTACK

I was sitting on my patio one day in mid-August thinking about Bobby and Trish down in Florida. It's amazing how we can think about someone and not long after they call or text. This coincidence no longer surprises me, so I just smiled and nodded when my phone buzzed about 10 minutes later with a text from Bobby. I always think of Einstein's wonderful quote, *"Coincidence is God's way of staying anonymous."*

> Bobby: hi sammy, just checking in. All is good here. Treatments going well. Some positive results. I feel stronger.
>
> Me: Great news, so happy for you. Look forward to seeing you soon.
>
> Bobby: me too. How are you?
>
> Me: Good, thanks
>
> Bobby: Trish and I are turning 60 a day apart next week. since I cannot travel, family and friends coming to FL this weekend to stay in a huge house we rented. Catered dinner on Saturday night.
>
> Me: Sounds Perfect. Have a fantastic birthday and soak in all that love!
>
> Bobby: I sure will, talk soon

Sunday afternoon a text came in from Bobby's phone, it wasn't from Bobby.

> Bobby: hi sammy, this is Trish, Bobby's wife. He asked me to text you. He had a heart attack last night.

I sat back in my chair, tears filling my eyes as I re-read the text a few times. *A heart attack?* I thought. *Man, he cannot catch a break.*

Me: oh trish, so sorry to hear this news. How is he?

Trish: In ICU and resting. Will be in touch when we know more

Me: OK, thanks, prayers sent your way. Give him a hug from me

Trish: Thank you. I will.

The day passed slowly, waiting for the next text. There certainly are times when life seems to really beat up on some people. They have their challenges, and are fighting the good fight, and then life throws another punch. I like to close my eyes and pray, and imagine my prayers floating out across the country or globe to the person I'm praying for; today my prayers floated to South Florida. The next day I received another text from Bobby's phone. It was Trish again.

Trish: hi Sammy. Bobby resting and feeling better. Drs running more tests. Think he can go back to the house in a few days. He probably didn't tell you he fell a few times before this, so drs are very cautious

Me: No, hadn't heard about falls. Thanks for letting me know. Do you know when you'll be back home from Florida?

Trish: not sure. Can't come soon enough. This definitely set him back and he needs rest, lots of it. Me or Bobby will stay in touch, and see you when we get back home.

* * *

Over a month later, on a crisp Fall afternoon, I pulled my car to the curb in front of Bobby & Trish's house. They had come home a few weeks after Bobby's heart attack, and were now focused on getting him back to his routine of working out so he could walk down the aisle at the March wedding. I walked around back of the house and saw Bobby sitting on the deck wearing a long sleeve t-shirt and sweatpants, his tall walker on wheels standing like a sentinel next to him. He was staring at the clear, peaceful water of a beautiful pool, with large stones on one side with a fountain playing its beautiful water music.

He smiled when he saw me. "Hey, Sammy."

I leaned down and gave him a kiss on the cheek. "Hi, my friend. How are you?" I asked as Trish came out of the house. Although we'd only met once briefly when she picked Bobby up after one of our meetings, she came to me, and we hugged. Her soft smile unable to hide her tired eyes. "I can't believe it . . . a heart attack?" I said before either of them could answer.

Bobby spoke, his speech slower and weaker than at our last meeting. He looked at Trish, wearing a smirk. "I don't like to call it a heart attack because there was no long-term damage to my heart; I was fortunate to have a great doctor who was able to remove the clot in a timely fashion which is why I call it a cardiac event." Trish rolled her eyes then held a cup holding one of the many daily powder drinks with a long straw so Bobby could take a sip. His hands lay still in his lap.

"Yes, okay, okay," Trish said. "Whatever we call it, it scared the hell out of all of us. We seemed to be headed in the right direction with the treatment down there, right, hon?" She rubbed Bobby's shoulder. "Then this." She took a deep breath, biting her lower lip, then looked to Bobby. "And so now we're going to get back into a routine, and he's excited to start working out again, and staying focused on the wedding in six months."

Bobby nodded to the walker. "Yep, we're gonna make it. Got my walker here and still able to get around." He looked to me, "I feel like I'm in a race against time . . . and I'm not stopping. I think a lot of St. Paul's quote when he said, 'I have fought the good fight, I have finished the race, I have kept the faith.' Well, my race isn't finished yet, so I'm still fighting the good fight and keeping the faith." Trish took a seat next to Bobby, placing her hand in his.

ANOTHER POLLYANNA PARTY

In December, the cold gray winter of the Northeast was upon us, and I was invited to Trish & Bobby's for their family Pollyanna party, a holiday tradition where each family member was assigned a person to whom they'd give a gift. They had been hosting this event for 25 years, and it was termed "legendary" by one of Trish's cousins.

When I arrived, I found the finished basement filled with smiling people. Festively wrapped presents were piled in corners and sat atop the bar. It looked more like a neighborhood Irish pub than someone's basement. The people ranged in age from newborn to ninety, and I could feel the love in the room. Bobby was leaning against the bar, his walker locked in place in front of him and his forearms resting on the elbow-height pads. Trish looked wonderful in a black skirt and cream silk blouse. I had the sense Bobby's ALS was on the back burner today and the focus was on family.

Trish and Bobby made their way slowly to a corner of the room, navigating small children playing on the floor who were waiting impatiently for the gift exchange. The room became quiet. "This is their welcome," one of Trish's seven brothers whispered to me. "It's always the best part of the day."

Trish kicked it off, welcoming everyone, and then going through a list of accomplishments of many in the room, from sports championships to academic achievements, to having babies and buying homes. I was inspired by the kindness of these two people; selfless in their love to recognize and lift up others. Then I was shocked as Trish came to me and grabbed my hand, pulling me up to stand with them as Bobby introduced me, saying it was also a tradition to welcome new friends here for the first time. I was forced to say a few words, struggling through joyful emotions, "Thank you, I'm absolutely blessed to be here and know these two beautiful people for the past year, and I'm sure you all know you're blessed to know them even longer."

When the list was done and the cheering and hooting subsided, Bobby spoke. "Trish and I also want to thank you all for your support as we continue on this journey. I've realized one of the best treatments for any illness is being with the people you love." He thanked his kids and a few others by name, then concluded, working hard to get the words out clearly. "We're going to keep fighting—" he paused, smiling slightly—"because we got a wedding happening soon." Trish hugged Bobby as tears flowed for many and the room erupted with cheers, and shouts of "We love you Trish and Doc." I said a quiet prayer, as Bobby walked by me slowly, deliberate in his steps, his arms and hands resting on his walker.

After a wonderful meal of chicken, steak, pasta, and much more, the gift exchange began. Trish stood in the corner holding a large box over her head. A few of the uncles began to bang out a drumroll on the bar. Bobby stood next to Trish, his mother-in-law next to him, rubbing his back.

"You all know what time it is now," she said.

The room erupted with chants of "Leather coat! Leather coat!," as Trish walked around the room like a boxer entering the ring. I turned to one of Trish's seven brothers and asked what was happening. He filled me in on the leather coat. One of their uncles, a bachelor, and generous man, blew out the Pollyanna gift limit of $30 many years ago when he gave one of the family a gift of a very expensive leather coat. Since then, 24 more have been given out. Trish's brother let me know that she "rigs" it to give it to a family member who's had a rough year.

I wonder if Bobby ever got it, I thought. Trish's brother smiled. "And I see what you're thinking. Trish and Bobby have already gotten one, and trust me, they deserve a helluva lot more." He winked with a tear in his eye as we turned back to the ruckus.

Trish announced the winner in dramatic fashion, and her teenage niece pulled the coat on and modeled it for the crowd. The party raged, the Miller Lites flowed, and after a while I decided it was time to head out so I made my way to Trish and Bobby. We chatted about the wonderful tradition they'd created and the love of family. On my way out I leaned in to kiss Bobby, "Great time, right? I'm really glad you were able to share a happy moment in our lives." We agreed to get together again soon.

* * *

We stayed in touch and Bobby kept me updated on his treatments. Trish had texted me about another fall he'd had. It was Valentine's weekend when he asked if I could stop by the house for a visit. I came in the back door and settled in with Bobby, who sat in a newer chair with a lift to help him get in and out easier.

"When we first met, you said you'd once heard an ALS patient describe her situation as a shitshow," I said. "How come you don't?"

Bobby put his feet on the floor then pushed and slid himself back in the chair, his arms still on his lap. "Sammy, listen, this is brutal. There are nights when I've cried with Trish, and days when sadness has wrapped me like a straitjacket, and it's hard to shake."

He looked intently at me. "I'm not afraid to die, I just don't want too yet. I guess if you think about the meaning of a shitshow, I'm in one, and my family as well. It's just that for me, I think there's a way for us to take the shit out of the show." I smiled at his phrasing that so closely echoed my own. "My shitshow is simply the way I think about my ALS. When I succumb to the physical disability and the negative forces of anger, chaos, despair, sadness, regret, lack of Faith . . . well, then I'm in the shitshow. However," Bobby winked at me, "and be sure to write this down—when I lean on my family, and my Faith, and when I fight like hell with my thoughts, and think about what *was* good, and what *is* good in my life now, and even what *will be* good tomorrow and the day after that and the day after that . . . well then, I take the shit out of the show. I just don't let it win and defeat my Spirit. For me, not letting the negative forces and facts of the situation win . . . that's the key to focus on."

"Wow," I said, amazed at this powerful insight Bobby just offered. "I like your focus on what was good in your life, what is good, and what will be good." The brutal facts are what they are; surrendering to them, and moving through them is the key.

Bobby continued, looking past me then back. He locked on my eyes. "Sammy, here's the thing that really supports me in fighting . . . I trust there is a Heaven, that place, that existence of peace and joy and love. I remember one time I was visiting the college where I played football because we were honoring our coach who was inducted into the college football hall of fame. I was in the stands after the ceremony and my group of friends and family were going to get some beers; I told them to go ahead without me and that I'd meet up with them. I sat in the stillness of that stadium, the only person in the stands, and I felt my dad." His smile was soft as he remembered this.

"I tell you, Sammy, there's no question my dad, his Spirit, Soul, energy, whatever you may call it . . . it was there with me, he . . . he was there. And man, was that an amazing feeling. So, I just trust this life is not all there is."

"I'm pretty sure that will be the case. And for now, you're here and you're still fighting and focused, right?"

"Yes." He reached under his leg and pulled a piece of paper out and handed it to me. I took it, my eyes staying on his. "Go ahead, read it. It's a prayer I wrote back when this all started. I say it many times a day."

Bobby's Prayer

Dear Jesus -

Grant me the strength to carry the cross You have asked me to bear.

I trust in You for better days, whether they be in this life or the next.

I ask for Your healing in any way You see fit. and in conformity to Your will.

And please provide Your enduring love and guidance to those around me, so they may adapt to the challenges this cross presents.

I ask this in Your name.

Amen

I read the prayer as my eyes filled, slowly lowering it to my lap afterward.

We sat in silence for a few minutes until Bobby raised his head and took a deep breath. "I'm scared of falling."

I turned my head slightly. "What?"

"I'm really scared of falling when I walk down the aisle. The wedding is just over a month away, and I don't know if I can do it. I don't want a wheelchair. It's my daughter's day, it's their day, and I don't want anything to affect that."

I moved to kneel next to Bobby, my hand on his, "Bobby. I hear you, and understand." He looked at me. "You've got to hold the focus that you'll walk down the aisle. You will."

His sad eyes looked away from me. "I don't know, Sammy, that's the plan."

Bobby's New Nemesis

A month later, Bobby's adversaries of time and sickness were joined by the powerful and unexpected forces of chaos, uncertainty, and a halt to social interaction . . . a worldwide pandemic called COVID-19. The pandemic many thought would not last long, intensified. His text—and I knew now Trish or someone else was texting for him—was this:

Bobby: hi Sammy. the wedding cancelled until May. how about this?

Me: yes, how are you?

Bobby: I'm disappointed

Me: can we talk?

Bobby: not now, we are trying to figure this out. Everyone is upset and we have to be really cautious about who visits because it would not be good if I got COVID

Me: I can't imagine how you all must feel. Promise me we can stay in touch? You have to keep fighting.

Bobby: OK

We stayed in touch as the world went on this crazy ride called COVID, and consistent chaos raged daily. I prayed for Bobby with the most intensity I think I ever had. In May the wedding was cancelled again and rescheduled for July; in June it was rescheduled for August. Plus, it would now be a small wedding with immediate family, as opposed to the original guest list of over two-hundred-fifty, bringing a monsoon of disappointment, sadness, and some anger.

As I thought about what he and Trish and his family were dealing with, I made a plea to visit.

> Me: Hi. can I come for a visit? We can do it outside, I'll wear a mask and stay far away
>
> Bobby: not sure, let me get back to you
>
> Me: OK, I understand

I heard nothing until a text came in a few hours later.

> Bobby: hi Sammy, it's Trish, I think a visit would do us good. can you come up tomorrow, 11 am?
>
> Me: sure, see you then

Bobby was sitting alone on the back deck when I walked around the corner. His mask was down, and his eyes were closed, so I stopped in my tracks. I stood, in awe of this man as he continued his battle against this brutal disease. A moment later he opened his eyes, turned his head to see me, and smiled softly. "Well, good morning, Sammy, it's been too long."

I pulled my mask down for a second and smiled back. "It sure has, wish I could hug you, I guess this will have to do for now." I put my arms in front of me and closed them in an "air hug" motion, and took a seat about six feet from Bobby.

We talked about COVID, and the disappointment of the past months of quarantine, and multiple wedding reschedules. Bobby looked to the smooth surface of the clear pool, then back to me. "I think I would have been good back in March, now five months have passed and I'm weaker. I don't think the day will be as initially envisioned. I'm trusting it will all work out." Just then Trish came out and we chatted for a few minutes. She looked exhausted: her hair was up, and she was wearing sweat pants and a t-shirt. She pulled Bobby's mask up, thanked me for visiting, and said she had to make some phone calls.

"You said a minute ago, you trust this works out. What is 'this'?" I asked.

Bobby took a deep breath. I had to lean in to hear his voice through the mask. "I guess everything. The wedding. My battle—our battle—with ALS."

I was quiet as we both turned our sight to the pool. "Bobby, I'm curious about something, mind if I offer you a simple exercise I do with my clients?"

"Sure, you know our talks are good for me."

"Close your eyes and see the word 'transition' written on a chalkboard, like the old ones the nuns used to use when you were back in grade school." He nodded, and I sensed that memory of the nuns brought a smile behind his mask. "Now add the letter 'h' between the letters 's' and 'i.'"

Bobby chuckled softly, "Transh . . . transhition?" He asked with the inflection of a question. "Is that even a word?" He opened his eyes.

"It is now." I tilted my head and raised my eyebrows. "Transition means to change from one state or condition to another, and you, and Trish and the kids are in the most challenging time of your lives." He nodded. "Well, remember when we talked about the shitshow and how you took the shit out of the show by not letting the physical challenge, and negative forces and thoughts win?" Another nod. "Well, I often ask my clients to take the shit out of their show, their transition, so to speak, by removing the 'h' from the word, right?"

"How do I do that?" He asked, shifting in his chairs, his arms still on his lap.

"Imagine that word on the chalkboard, and you walk up and cross out the letter 'h'."

He closed his eyes, then looked to me, his eyes misty above his mask. "Thank you."

"For what?"

"For allowing me to imagine walking again and lifting a piece of chalk to write on the board."

My eyes filled, and I wiped them quickly. "Sure. So, when you cross out the 'h' you have to think of a negative word that begins with 'h' that you want to remove from your thinking, from how you're dealing with your challenge."

Bobby nodded, "OK, got it. Give me a minute."

I sat still, giving Bobby all the time he needed as I watched birds darting among the trees and bushes surrounding the pool.

"Not sure I can come up with one."

"Okay, remember you've asked me to write some of our conversations down? So as maybe to support others on a similar journey to yours?" He nodded, "Let me suggest that you've already removed a negative "h" word."

"I have?"

"Yes, hope."

"Hope? Hope what?"

"It seems to me you've removed the 'h' by removing hope as your focus. Now I know this may sound crazy, stay with me. What other verb could a person use instead of *hoping* that something will happen? You're *blank* that something will happen." I said, emphasizing the word blank.

Bobby scanned the backyard, "Hmmm, you got me here. I always thought of hope as a good thing. Not sure why I'd want to remove that."

"Trust," I finally said to him.

His eyes locked on mine as he thought about what I offered him, then they narrowed as he turned again to scan the yard. "Yes. Trust," he said quietly.

I continued, leading with his name to get his attention. "Bobby, I've worked with many people who have shifted from using the word hope, to replacing it with trust. You do that."

"Hope is a good thing for many people, although the thing about hope is it's defined as *wanting something to happen."* I paused as his eyes filled with curiosity. "Trust, for me, is more intentional. It's defined as a firm belief in the reliability, truth, ability, or strength of someone or something. Hope—for me—has a passiveness to it, as if we just sit and wait for the outcome. Trust, however, has an energy to it, that firm belief thing, and the word's ability and strength to it that call us to action."

I let Bobby sit with my statement for a minute, until he replied. "I see what you mean, Sammy. I learned a long time ago our words have energy to them. Think about this, should I *hope* to walk our daughter down the aisle? Or am I better to hold a firm belief in my ability and strength to walk our daughter down the aisle?" He nodded slowly; his eyes fixed on mine. "Should I *hope* Heaven is real? Or should I trust it's there, waiting for all of us?"

I led Bobby's lesson one step further. "Yes, I like it. Here's what I do with people sometimes. Say, 'I hope I'll walk our daughter down the aisle. Then, say, 'I trust I'll walk our daughter down the aisle.'" He said these.

"Now say, 'I hope there's a heaven.' Then, 'I trust there's a heaven.'"

Bobby said all four of those statements a few times. "In case you can't tell," he said, "I'm smiling behind this mask. I feel a lot better with the trust statement, and this is why I've come to use it. I also thought of the verse in Proverbs I like: *Trust in the Lord with all your heart and lean not on your own understanding. In all your ways acknowledge Him, and He will make your path straight."*

"Sure, remember the first time we met, and you told me you could run *from* or *to* your Faith?" He nodded. "Well, that's trust. Faith is simply *belief without proof*."

"It sure is. I guess that's why our money says. 'In God we trust,' not 'In God we hope.'"

"Ha ha," I laughed. "Yes, I guess so. What we must remember is action is so needed to drive the things we trust will occur, and most people admit that most of the time they act from how they feel. So, we must use words and statements to put us into positive feelings, so we take the action we need to take."

"Sounds simple."

"In theory for sure. We just need to stay aware of it, and make sure we have the support to act this way. I encourage people to maybe experiment with it a bit, and see if there's value in it for them, you already know the value."

"Something just came to mind; can I share it with you?" he said.

"Of course." I replied, scooting my chair slightly closer to Bobby.

"I remember this woman who I operated on; she developed an infection and got really sick. After a week of intensive treatment, all of her medical parameters stabilized, but she would just not wake up. I talked with my colleagues, and nothing made sense; we just couldn't figure it out. Then on Saturday two weeks later, I took a small figure of an angel Trish had given me, and I placed it in her hand, and whispered in her ear, 'It's time to wake up.'" Bobby paused, recalling the incident, and I remained in silent anticipation. He looked to me, smiling softly. "On Sunday she woke up. Yeah Sammy, I don't hope there's a Heaven, I trust there is."

I sat, smiling at the beautiful story that moved beyond the medical side of patient care.

Bobby asked, "How about helpless? I feel so helpless sometimes, because I cannot control so much of what I have to deal with."

"Sure, so what's the opposite of helpless? What word could you focus on to get rid of your helplessness?"

"I guess empowered," he replied. I nodded. "Regardless of what I'm facing I can always choose my thoughts. I'm always empowered to pray, to remember some good times, to be thankful for something in my life right now." He paused, "I see what you mean."

"Yes, I've used this simple model of taking the 'h' out to get people to examine their perspective. I mean, I see transhition as another word for shitshow, right?"

"I understand; this is good. While the reality is I'm helpless to do some things, I can focus on all that I can do. Thanks, Sammy."

Trish came out to sit with us, "How's it going?"

"All good, Sammy and I had a great talk. As always, she's given me something to think about."

"Well, I think I've learned more from the two of you in how to handle tough times, you're both really amazing people." Trish leaned in and gave Bobby a kiss on the head.

"Well," I said, "I've to get going, and you all have a wedding in a few weeks. Bobby, remember, trust. Trust you'll walk down that aisle. And one more thing, there's a movie, *Meet Joe Black*, starring Brad Pitt and Anthony Hopkins. In a nutshell, Brad Pitt is death, and he's come to get Anthony Hopkins, a kind, wonderful, man who happens to be a billionaire. At the end, as Pitt takes Hopkins on a walk over a bridge, Hopkins stops and turns and asks, 'Should I be afraid?' Pitt stops, and replies, 'Not a man like you.'"

I stood, stretching out my arms to both of them, "Enjoy the wedding. Love you guys." The three of us glanced to one another, eyes full of tears, as I turned and walked away.

The Walk

The wedding day arrived with a stifling heat that felt more like New Orleans than suburban Philadelphia. Bobby/Trish and I texted as I wished them a wonderful day and they said they were ready. While I wasn't entirely sure if Bobby would walk their daughter down the aisle, trust me, I was not going to miss it if he did. A few hours before the ceremony I snuck in the back of the church and up to a dark corner of the choir loft. I essentially made myself invisible to anyone who may glance in my direction. The altar was surrounded with large pots of white roses and carnations, and the sun showed brightly through the colored stain glass windows.

The music began, the small crowd in the first few pews turned, and as I peered down the aisle, I saw Bobby and Trish's daughter being walked up the aisle by her youngest brother. He walked her a little way, then turned her over to her next oldest brother, who in turn walked her up the aisle a bit more, turning her over to her oldest brother. With not much aisle left until the bride was to be joined with her waiting groom, I saw the youngest brother hurrying up the side aisle and through a pew to where Bobby stood against a pew, supported by another man. Bobby moved to the center of the aisle with his youngest son supporting him with both hands from behind, and his daughter took his arm as tears filled all eyes in the church. And so, through more than a year of battling his debilitating disease, and another unexpected, five months moving through the once-in-a-lifetime, catastrophic, and destructive event called COVID-19 . . . Bobby walked his daughter down the aisle. She kissed his cheek, as smiles blended with tears, and Bobby handed her off to the young man who would become his fourth son.

As you can imagine, the nuptial mass was absolutely perfect, a modern-day fairy tale.

After the wedding the bridal party grabbed refreshments and stood in the stone grotto in front of the church as carloads of well-wishing family and friends processed by to celebrate and take part in this joyful day. Bobby sat in a chair, and with his tuxedo and his slicked-back gray hair, he resembled a handsome, 60-ish movie star. When the last car had cruised slowly by, the wedding party made their way to the waiting open air trolley, I walked quickly to the window next to where Bobby sat, and with tears in my eyes, called out, "Hey handsome." He turned and smiled as masks were not happening today. "You did it my friend, you did it."

Bobby smiled and replied with a wink, "Yes, Sammy, we did. Thanks for everything." I smiled, unable to respond. Trish leaned over, absolutely radiant in her navy dress, and gave me a thumbs up. "And Sammy," Bobby nodded, "it's all gonna be okay." I blew him a kiss as the trolley slowly pulled away.

(Author's note: Bobby's chapter is the only one in this book based on a real life story. He and my sister, Trish, are amazing people. Visit this link to see Bobby's walk, Trish, and the rest of the family on this special day.

https://mediazilla.com/rQ5hTFqURk

Just an Angel on a Cloud

"The world breaks everyone and afterward many are strong at the broken places."

- Ernest Hemingway

Sammy's Sign Off

So, there are my seven clients. Well, not really clients; as I've said before, they're now my friends, and I'm blessed to be able to support them on their journeys, and work to have them take the shit out of their shows, and develop the capacity to move through the brutally difficult challenges of life . . . to build resilience.

St. Paul, The Apostle, wrote these words near the end of his life: *"I have fought the good fight, I have finished the race, I have kept the faith."* They remind me of the work I do now. While my friends—and perhaps you—are not near the end of your life (do we really know?), you will have struggles, that's just part of living your life.

How is life for you right now? What's your level of fulfillment? Any shitshows you're dealing with? If so, think about how the stories of the people in this book connected with and inspired you. Perhaps one of my friends is in a similar struggle to one you're facing, and they planted seeds of courage and inspiration for you to keep going . . . to see the other side of your struggle.

Maybe it was Alexis, and her move from being hunkered down for a fight when she believed she was trapped by resentment towards her ex-husband to *Let'sooooooo*. Getting clear on what she wanted and staying focused on that allowed Alexis to taking the actions required to achieve her vision.

Maybe it was Nigel (and/or his beautiful daughter, Chloe) as he moved from hating all that had happened and was happening to him to focusing on what he could choose to love about his life. Dylan certainly gives us all some things to consider as you evolve into who you are, and you do this sometimes when those you love, those close to you, don't accept or agree. His move from hiding, to the courage he develops to move into who he really is can inspire many of you on a similar journey.

Jill (and Arjun) have encountered what I believe to be life's greatest pain, the loss of a child. Think about loved ones you've lost, and the pain, and feelings of not wanting to go on, or not knowing how to move on with your life. Jill certainly supports you in your own struggles to move from this intense and often paralyzing hurt, to step onto the path of healing, of seeing the hurt differently, to seeing it as one of many steps on this path of healing.

Natalie offers us a strong reminder of asking ourselves the question, "How am I contributing to this shitshow that I'm blaming on other people?" Her struggle to see that *hanging* on to our past can sometimes prevent us from *moving* on. Sometimes, it's only after we create space in our lives that something new may enter, and take root, and grow . . . and create fulfillment for us.

The courageous young Jess is a perfect example for us all to remember the timeless insight offered us by Dr. Victor Frankl, author of the classic work *Man's Search for Meaning*. Frankl, a WWII concentration camp survivor wrote: "The last of the human freedoms: to choose one's attitude in any given set of circumstances, to choose one's own way." I strongly support a person with deep depression and anxiety to get professional support. I also know there are things you can do to strengthen your approach to building strategies and overcoming your anxiety.

Bobby and Trish are just wonderful. The courage and Faith they lean on as their foundation for fighting their struggle should be something always taken to heart; something to work to always incorporate into your life—during the good times, and the struggles. Hope is a good thing, it means to want something, whereas trust is a firm belief in something or someone. Bobby's move from hope to trust is something we all need to remember. Next time you hear yourself using the word hope in a sentence, stop and repeat the sentence, replacing hope with trust, you'll likely be glad you did. Our words have energy tied to our emotions, feelings and subsequently the actions we take. Go back to Bobby's Prayer and maybe print it out, or take a picture of it on your phone . . . and pray it. Pray it for others who are in a struggle, and pray it for yourself. Bobby told me he is 100% fine with that . . . wink!

So, you will likely find you can take the shit out of your show by identifying one of the "h" words in this book that is your barrier. Ask how you can move from that, to something else, some other much more positive focus. If another word shows up for you that does not begin with an 'h,' great. Work to eliminate that one, and replace it with another.

Keep this book, go back, and refer to the stories, and the subsequent possibilities to see your shitshow differently, to build your resilience and take the shit out of your show.

Now I must leave. I only come back here when I'm needed. I'm always available if you ever want to send a prayer to me. I've got a smile on my face as I cruise down the highway, top down, sun out, and the breeze blowing my hair beneath my jckrbbt hat. I take the sun pendant hanging from my neck in my fingers, caressing it gently, and look to my left, to a minivan with a woman driver and a few young girl passengers. The looks of disbelief on their faces always makes me smile as I hit the gas, and disappear . . . just an angel floating away on a cloud.

Made in the USA
Monee, IL
27 October 2021